to Paula

CONTACTO SILVESTRE ediciones
de Santiago G. de la Vega
Av. del Libertador 1396 - Piso 6º B
B1638BEZ - Vicente López, Buenos Aires, Argentina.
Ph/Fax (54 11) 4795-1727
www.contactosilvestre.com.ar

PATAGONIA, the LAWS of the FOREST

I.S.B.N. 987-21141-0-2
Queda hecho el depósito que marca la ley 11.723

Title in Spanish:
PATAGONIA, las LEYES del BOSQUE
First published 1999; second edition 2001; third edition 2003.
First english edition 2003.

Illustrations of Flora and Fauna
Gustavo R. Carrizo
Cover illustrations from the educational poster *Bosque patagónico*,
by Aldo Chiappe, Fundación Vida Silvestre Argentina.

Translation: Richard Primrose

Graphic Design
Verónica Martorell
Cover design, Jorge Garcia, Trazos S.R.L.

Printed in
Gráfica LAF S.R.L.
Loyola 1654 C1414AVJ, Buenos Aires, Argentina
Ph: (54 11) 4855-8171 / (54 11) 49543893

Published December 2003, Buenos Aires, Argentina.

PATAGONIA
The LAWS of the FOREST

Santiago G. de la Vega

IIllustrations: Gustavo R. Carrizo and Aldo Chiappe

Let's Start with Hawaii

¡¡Aloha!! (Welcome)...

There is a land with seashores where blue waves dance, with beaches where warm winds blows, and where people just enjoy life surfing and smiling. Who hasn't dreamed with an almost paradise image like this of Hawaii?

What does this idyllic place have to do with the Southern Beech Forests in *Argentina* and *Chile*?
Let's see. The first Hawaiian Islands emerged in the immense Pacific Ocean at least 30 million years ago. They are at a distance of 3,500 km from the closest continent, being the extreme geographical isolation in the world.

The Southern Beech Forests in *Argentina* and *Chile* may be considered a green archipelago, and it has been isolated from other forests since 10 million years. The closest grow at present in the Northwest of *Argentina*: those who travel from the *Yungas* subtropical cloud forest have experienced the distance of more than 1,200 km of arid and beautiful landscape (through *Catamarca*, *La Rioja*, *San Juan*, *Mendoza* and *Neuquén* provinces) including the Patagonian steppe, till they can exclaim: "Forest in sight".

The point is that both environments, Hawaii and the Southern Beech Forests, share a clue concept: they are **I-S-L-A-N-D-S**, and in both cases isolated since a long time ago.

With the geographic isolation the forces of evolution may act faster and result more evident. It is considered that many of the ecological and evolutionary processes applicable to Hawaii, the *Galapagos* and

5

other archipelagos are valid in most of the isolated terrestrial environments. This applies in our Southern Beech Forests, with obvious differences, but the concept is valid. One of the consequences of isolation is the high number of endemism (see page 13).

Which plants and animals species are there? Where did they originate? Why are some only found there and why not elsewhere? Charles Darwin (1809-1882) and Alfred Russel Wallace (1823-1913) dedicated their lives to find answers to the interrelation of the fascinating natural world. They spent years collecting data and samples, and observing live in continents and islands. With study and analysis as well as passion and imagination, they gave origin to theories.

After them (…and their theories), more discoveries followed, new connections and interpretations and more questions.
In the first steps of the XXI century we may conclude diverse balances of the world we live in. But we must consider it a privilege to exist in a time of knowledge. With this perspective, a trip to the Southern Beech Forests may be a fabulous adventure.

These pages give the chance of a practical use on the field itself, with many examples of plants and animals. So that they don't remain isolated observations, the proposal is to try to fit the pieces of a dynamic and changing system together. To know the branches is undoubtedly attractive, but I think and feel that trying to see the "forest" is even more captivating and motivating.

Santiago G. de la Vega
Biologist, avid for Nature

Contents

Let's start with Hawaii

I) Presentation

II) The Laws of the Forest

III) Along the paths of the Forest

Flora

Presentation (I)

The rules of the game: How to use "The Laws..."

The Laws... pretends to explain the rules of the game in a simple and pleasant style. There are comments and comparisons with concepts easy to visualise which help to remember ideas.

On different occasions I make reference to the forests in the Northern Hemisphere or other environments comparing them to the Southern Beech Forests.

It is difficult to visualise the geological time taken for the long lasting processes during which many of the evolutionary changes take place. We

Austral Pigmy Owl

don't see what a butterfly, which lives a short life, may see as regards the changes between winter and summer. But we can look for evidence. There are examples in the relations brought by the coevolution. May it be between flowers and animals that pollinate them, the fruits and those who spread their seeds, or the interaction between prey and predator.

As regards the environmental changes, the grains of pollen with their great distribution and resistance, represent a library of information for researchers. It's possible to know to what type of plant they belonged and from there infer the climate in past times. The "prints" left by the glaciations are more at hand for those who travel the Andean Patagonian region.

This book is prepared to be used before, during and after the walks in the forest in the following way:

Before:
Go through the *Presentation* and the Laws of the Forest.

During:
The section *Along the Paths of the Forest* will be the main connection between your observations and the contents. It's

clear that it is not the same to go along a path in the Fueguian forest than in the area of the Valdivian forest. Without forgetting the differences, the text pretends to offer interpretation tools that are valid in each case.

The cross references are shown indicating the corresponding page number.

After:
With your observations in situ, it is advisable to go over the different topics again. With more time to think, you will be able to connect your experiences in a better way.
At the end, think about the section *Us as part of Nature.*

Attitudes and suggestion for the walks in the Forest:

- Observe and relate. **OBSERVE** and **RELATE**.
- To observe flowers, seeds, fruits or leaves, don't tear them off the plants.
- The flowers are more numerous in spring.
- The fruits are at their best towards the end of summer.
- The fungi are abundant in autumn.
- The variation of the altitude above sea level implies the greatest variation in the vegetation as you go along a path.
- A magnifying glass helps appreciate details and discover a new world, especially flowers and insects.
- To observe the object of your interest with the binoculars up side down is a good method to improvise a magnifying glass.
- Binoculars are indispensable for birdwatching, even though some species can be watched without them.
- Dawn and dusk are the best moments to explore the paths to look for fauna, especially birds.
- Many of the examples of flora and fauna mentioned in this book are illustrated and I also mention their areas of distribution. Even more, it is very convenient to ask the local people about "who is who" or where is it possible to find "this..." or "that..."

The players: Species

First clue concept: **S-P-E-C-I-E-S**. They are a group of individuals of common ancestry that closely resemble each other, that can interbreed and leave fertile offspring. The most important characteristic they have in common is their genetic information, which is unique.

This concept defines the vertebrates quite well. But bacteria, plants and invertebrates are some of the living groups that are furthest away from conventions. And let's not talk about fossils. That is why, there may be different points of view if a botanist, zoologist, geneticist or a palaeontologist give their opinion on the topic. In spite of this, it is valid and enlightening to have it in mind as a starting point.

Because of their isolation (see page 5), the flora and fauna of the Southern Beech Forests have many **E-N-D-E-M-I-C** groups. This means that evolved in and has remained restricted to a region. For example in our area and among trees, the *Alerce* and the Andean Cypress are endemic; and between the mammals, the *Pudu* (Cervidae) and the *Güiña* (Felidae).

Relict species are those that have been reduced in number by natural causes and survive in reduced areas. Examples of this type are: *Araucaria* and *Alerce*.

Key species are those that are vital for the cohesion of the community. Examples among birds are: Green-backed Firecrown as a pollinator, and White-crested Elaenia as a seed disperser (see page 81).

In reference to the strategies of the species there are two basic tendencies: The **pioneer** species, wich are generalist, good colonisers and with a great capacity to spread. But at a high cost: they produce a great number of young but few survive. Some pioneer species can benefit with man's action (see page 102).

The **specialised** species are fewer in number, with a smaller capacity to

Pehuén

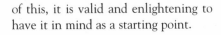

13

spread and colonise new areas. They have a small offspring but with a great chance to survive. In general, they have higher risk of extinction as result of human acivities.

The names of the species:

In the text I use the common name of the species, except when it is more convenient to use the latin scientific names, especially genus (include one or more species) or family (include one or more genus). At the end of the book there is a list of common names and corresponding latin names (see page 123).

With the latin names the main goal is to unify criteria. It allows us, among other things, to compare groups from different continents. Like this we can tell that the *Lenga* and *Ñire* are found from *Neuquén* to *Tierra del Fuego*. If we go to New Zealand, we can learn that beeches are there a dominating group of trees. But when we find out that the

Male

Torrent Duck

Female

Lenga, the *Ñire* and beeches from New Zealand belong to the *Nothofagus* genus, we have a connection!
And there are immediate questions: How can there be trees of the same genus, which grow wild in different continents thousands of miles away? Did they land from Noah's Arc at different ports? Is there any acceptable explanation? (see page 18).

Important concepts to remember:
    ... endemic
    ... relict
    ... key
    ... pioneer
    ... specialised

The playing field: the Patagonian Forests

I'm calling Southern Beech Forests to the areas of Subantarctic Forests that cover areas from *Argentina* and *Chile*.
In *Argentina*, they get the name of Patagonian Forests (see map in color page I).

They protect the soil and the river basins, regulate the water cycle and the microclimate, maintain biodiversity, and of course, fill our soul!

Origin, isolation and evolution

Flora shake cocktail with ice (and no lemon). Secret: millions years of evolution.

Ingredients:

I include some of the genus that arrived from different places long time ago. As a reference, in each case I mention the latin name with its corresponding common name of the well known plants of these days.

• Elements that arrived before the origin of the Andes (around 60 million years ago) from the tropical rainforests in America:

"pioneer"	"descendants"	
Genus name	Latin name	Common name
Azara	Azara lanceolata	Corcolén
Chusquea	Chusquea culeou	Colihue cane
Drimys	Drimys winter	Winter's bark
Escallonia	Escallonia rubra	Siete camisas

• Many important groups were originated at a different time, at least 45 million years ago and in the southern edge of the ancient mega continent Gondwana:

"pioneer"	"descendants"	
Genus name	Latin name	Common name
Araucaria	Araucaria araucana	Pehuén
Aristotelia	Aristotelia maqui	Maqui
Blechnum	Blechnum pennamarina	Punque (fern)
Gevuina	Gevuina avellana	Avellano
Lomatia	Lomatia ferruginea	Fuinque
Podocarpus	Podocarpus nubigena	Maniú Macho
Nothofagus	Nothofagus pumilio	Lenga
	Nothofagus antarctica	Ñire
	Nothofagus dombeyi	Coihue
	Nothofagus betuloides	Guindo
	Nothofagus nervosa	Raulí
	Nothofagus obliqua	Roble Pellín

• On the other hand, with the formation of the Andes and the cold Humboldt Current from the Pacific Ocean, more groups of plants appeared. Also, some elements from the ecosystems adjacent to the temperate forests, Coming from the Northern Hemisphere along the Andean corridor.

"pioneer"	"descendants"	
Genus name	Latin name	Common name
Ribes	*Ribes magellanicum*	Parilla
Empetrum	*Empetrum rubrum*	Murtilla
Berberis	*Berberis buxifolia*	Calafate

When the mega continent of Gondwana split, the flora and fauna evolved in new sceneries: South America, Antarctica, Australia, New Zealand, Tasmania and New Guinea.

The distribution of the forests that grew in Antarctica and neighbouring lands, suggests that the white continent was the origin and center of distribution of most of the forests that now grow in the south of *Argentina*, *Chile*, *Australia*, *Tasmania* and the south of Africa.

Stages of more uniform climate allowed a wide distribution of a variety of flora groups. It is the case of the *Araucaria* genus, represented today in *Argentina* by the *Pino Paraná* in the *Misiones* Subtropical Rainforest, and the *Pehuén* in *Neuquén* Province.

In our Southern Beech Forests the evergreen trees dominate, even though there are deciduous species of *Nothofagus*. This characteristic in some *Nothofagus* was originated in past times under colder conditions.

Great catastrophes occurred, and new opportunities arose. Little by little, the flora started to become isolated. Different Pleistocene glaciers advance (see page 39), caused new isolations, and the austral Andes acted as a physical barrier.

The actual climate, therefore the one that regulates the basic distribution of the vegetation, appears since barely 3000 years ago.

Michay

17

Continental drift and plate tectonics

Alfred Wegener (1880-1930) was the first to realise that the continents drift exposing his arguments in the book *The Origin of the Continents and Oceans*, published in 1915. His ideas were not accepted till over 30 years later. The book has been considered a key reference for Geology because of the depth of its content, similarly compared to what Darwin's *The Origin of the Species* means to Biology. Wegener recognises at least twenty plate tectonics (from the greek term that means construct) in the whole world. Some are found in the ocean beds and others have continents over them.

In our region, the Nazca plate (under the Southwest Pacific Ocean), moves an average of 2.5 cm per year towards the east, and the South American plate (under our continent) moves slightly more than one cm each year towards the west. The formation of the *Andes*, earthquakes and volcanic eruptions has a close relation with these movements. The question is, how have they occurred, and how have the continental masses been affected?

200 million years ago: the continent Pangaea starts to break up. Laurasia in the Northern Hemisphere and Gondwana in the Southern Hemisphere are formed.

65 million years ago: close connection between South America and Antarctica. Australia and New Zealand are separated from Antarctica. Madagascar splits from Africa.

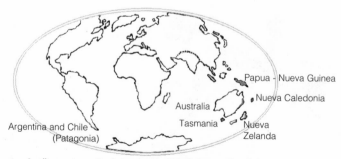

Papua - Nueva Guinea

Nueva Caledonia

Australia

Tasmania

Nueva Zelanda

Argentina and Chile (Patagonia)

Actual days: since 3 million years ago, South America joined North America through Central America. The areas where Nothofagus forests are found in the world today are mention in the map.

Random Games and something else: from cards to genetic variation

Setting: magnificent and peaceful sunset in the forest, soft breeze creating music among the leaves of the trees. Let's add some fun: two couples playing a game of *Truco*. (Note: *Truco* is almost a national sport and it is played with spanish cards. If you don't know the rules you can ask...)

First hand:
Envido
Falta envido!
Quiero! (I accept)
Thirty two, they answer.
Thirty three! you shout and win.

Next hand:
Truco
Quiero retruco
¡Quiero vale cuatro!

Your ace of spades beats your rival's ace of clubs.
(Don't feel too proud, it was all set up).

Halftime: The soft breeze becomes a bit stronger and five cards are blown away without anybody realising. (the ace of spades and the four sevens).
It will now be impossible to receive some of the good cards and combine them to play a good game, and you have to consider that each card can have more than one use. On the one hand, the probability of getting bad cards has increased. Surely, your game will not be as favourable as before.

In this metaphorical comparison I want to help you fix and clarify concepts. Let's go from truco to a group of huemules, one of our two species of native deer in the region (see page 93).

Huemul

If there is a diverse genetic pool (full deck), with the combination of genetic material from mothers and fathers in each generation, individuals of the group are best adapted to changing environmental conditions. The genetic recombination (let's say that it corresponds to the combination of the cards each player receives per hand) is the immediate and most important source of the genetic variation in each member that reproduces sexually. Due to environmental conditions, natural selection determines that only some survive, grow and reproduce.

But the present populations of huemules are scarce (although the exact numbers are not known, it is estimated that there are ten populations in *Argentina* and *Chile*), and in general they are isolate from each other. Their genetic pools could be incomplete and the isolation determines little interaction between neighbouring populations. Another problem is interbreeding. The *Huemul* is not the only one in such a critical situation. The *Huillín* (see page 99) is also in danger.

Huillín

The risks of being so few

In isolated environments, the populations are small and in greater danger of becoming extinct. In good years there will be large offspring and high young survival rate; in bad ones, mortality can increase due to causes as lack of food, intense snowfalls or volcanic ashes.

On the other hand, we must point out the difference between populations. For example, an important variable for the huemules is the proportion of sexes. If we consider a population of 15 males and 5 females, the expectancy of offspring is smaller than that of a group of 5 males and 15 females (the numbers are just exemplary).

Among forest tree species, little is known about the genetic variation (how complete or incomplete the deck is).

The number of adaptations of organs and tissue of various species give an idea that there might be great genetic variation. But it is not the only determinant, there is also plasticity (in Truco you can also do well even though your cards are not good).

For example, the Lenga, the Ñire and the Firebush (distributed from

Neuquén to *Tierra del Fuego*) have different shapes and sizes according to the changes in latitude and altitude, as you will be able to prove. A 30 mts tall Lenga tree in the fuegian forests looks very different to a Lenga which is one meter tall on the timberline of the Lanín volcano.

Lengas with different shapes

The *Roble Pellín* (see page 55) shows a great variability in many of its features. In *Chile* it was proved that the higher up a mountainside they grow (therefore exposed to greater drought), the largest the size and weight of their seeds: they can develop much quicker, with deeper and longer roots in order to obtain water and nutrients.

In *Chile*, two close groups of Winter's bark (see page 56) showed differences in production such as:

• at 700 mts. above sea level, good drainage soil: 168,000 seeds/kg.
• at 20 mts. above sea level, bad drainage soil: 336,000 seeds/kg.

Others have adaptations to the intense snowfall. *Alerces* with narrow crowns, with column structure and flexible branches can resist the weight of the snow without breaking off, and the open crowns of the *Araucaria* with narrow branches wouldn't allow the snow to accumulate on its branches.
Trees must adapt to illnesses and the attack of certain insects or parasites. They can elaborate resistant tissue, toxic substances or a system to block the entry of the enemy.

21

The laws of the forest (II)

The leaves of the trees

In the Southern Beech Forests we find mostly evergreen flowering trees (see page 51). In the forests of the Northern Hemisphere, in contrast, pines (conifers) dominate.

Our conifers (see page 49) aren't pines. The conifers as a group are well adapted to resist the lack of water, low temperature, strong winds and intense snowfalls.
Their narrow leaves, covered in wax and impregnated in resin, don't allow excessive transpiration. They have a high concentration of fenolic acid or lignin and a high proportion of fibres. These components determine a low decomposition of the leaves when they fall down. We can probe this for example when we walk through an *Araucaria* or Andean Cypress forest.

Among the flowering trees, the evergreens also have a high proportion of fibres. For the evergreen *Coihue* (leaves of gradual replacement) the decomposition is slow (approximately 17 % per year). For the *Ñire* and Lenga (deciduous) the decomposition is fast (56 % annually).

The orange and red tone colours of autumn in the *Lenga*, the *Ñire* (from *Neuquén* to *Tierra del Fuego*), the *Raulí* and the *Roble Pellín* (in

Leaves of the Pehuén

23

Argentina, in the Lanín National Park area), seduce and enchant everyone. What determines the change leaves coloration?

Temperature could control the growth of leaves, their size and their falling, but variation of hours of sunlight is the clue that regulates the change in colour.

If they didn't shed their leaves before winter, probably their crowns wouldn't resist the heavy weight of snow on their foliage, and the requirements of water and nutrients wouldn't satisfy the roots that remain in the frozen ground. On the other hand, shedding their leaves is an antique inheritance, brought about by severe environmental conditions.

"Look after your pennies that the pounds will look after themselves"

There are trees that are adapted to not losing nutrients, especially if these are scarce in the soil. The *Guindo* (see page 54) for example, transports nutrients to the stem before the leaves fall.

The leaves of the Lenga fall in autumn, and between 40 % and 60 % of the essential nutrients they possess like potassium, nitrogen, and phosphorous are also taken to the stem to keep them.

The seduction of the flowers

Flowers contain sexual reproduction organs of the plants. The grain of pollen in the masculine flower must reach the ovule of the feminine flower for the fecundation and a seed to be formed.

In many cases, both sexes are in the same flower, but only a few can self pollinate.

Plants produce flowers once or many times a year, and once or more times during the existence of the plant. There are also extremists: from plants that flower only one day a year to those that do so every day in the year.

The first flowers

The first flowering plants (Angiosperms) appeared around 120 million years ago. They had two great advantages over the conifers:

• The ovule is protected in the ovary, future fruit (means greater protection against predators or severe environmental conditions).

• Their dispersion is more effective including close interrelation with animals, especially insects.

The conifers, on the other hand, have a poor capacity to protect their ovule, and don't develop real fruit (they produce cones). They depend much on the wind for their dispersion.

In the Southern Beech Forests, different factors regulate the appearance of flowers: water availability, the changes in temperature, the duration of snow covering the plants or the variation of daylight hours.

Quintral

"Gone with the Wind". First part

"Take advantage of our flight plan, we take you any place". This seems to be what the wind offers the plants. Uncountable transported passengers (pollen grains among them) for thousands of years prove this, but only a few reach destinies.

The grains of pollen must be light and have an adequate shape and size. Furthermore, they must be liberated before the rainy season because precipitation eliminates them completely from the air. Moreover, the direct action of ultra-violet rays can result fatal.

In the forest, the trees can be barriers for air transport, although most of them being pollinated by the wind flower before the leaves appear, to take advantage of the free air space.

On the other hand, the Patagonian wind blows in a seasonal pattern, dominating in spring and the beginning of summer. They transport the pollen from the *Nothafagus* and Conifers. Pollen liberation is very noticeable in the Andean Cypress.

Among conifers in general, the masculine cones surge before the feminine ones, adaptation that favours crossed pollination (this means, between different trees) and the consequent genetic variability (see page 19). This occurs frequently between plants with separate sex flowers, like the Nothofagus.

Attention: Animals pollinating

When the diversity of plants is high and the distance between members to be pollinated is great, the dispersion by wind isn't so effective. This is the case of the *Misiones* subtropical rainforest (includes the area of the Iguazu falls) or the *Yungas* subtropical cloud forest, Northwesten *Argentina*. A variety of relations surged from the coevolution with animals ensures a more effective pollination. In the Southern forests, especially in the Valdivian Forest, this type of relations is very important.

The pollinating insects and birds do a door to door mail service from which seeds are formed. Some plants are more productive when the mail repeats its visit.

Pollinating insects

The shape, colour, smell, structure and size of the flowers seduce the pollinating insects. Furthermore, the plants invest energy to produce and offer nectar, pollen and other substances like oils and pheromones.

The combination of flower colours is usually yellow and blue, yellow and violet, orange and blue. The insects can view the ultra-violet in their

the adequate insect. The colourful species of the genus *Mutisia* (see page 66), are a good example among the native Composite in the Valdivian Forest.

The plants pollinated by insects tend to have a one or two months a year seasonal flowering. This is the case of the *Ulmo* (*Lago Puelo* National Park), *Palo Santo* (Puerto Blest), *Sauco del Diablo* (*Lanín* National Park to *Los Glaciares* National Park).

The Pollination by Birds

visual spectre. Yellow is the colour that they recognise the most, and red the one they distinguish the least. On the other hand, their visual perception is not good. The flowers evolved in a variety of shapes (cut off, with edges, etc.) helping their differentiation. The beautiful flower of the Amancay may be an example.

There has been a tendency in flowers from various groups of plants to reduce in size and form inflorescences. In them, the peripheral flowers are sterile and modified to attract the insect, while the central ones are for reproduction. They can ensure in this way the pollination of various flowers at the same time. The "sun" from the sunflower (Compositae family) includes up to one thousand flowers and in one flight, hundreds can be pollinated by

Among the birds of the Patagonian Forests, the Green-backed Firecrown (see page 77) is practically the only exclusively pollinator species. They are seduced by red or pink flowers, with a long and tubular corolla and abundant diluted nectar.

Mutisia decurrens

27

Firebush

Chilco

Many of these flowers are creepers and epiphytes (see page 61), with an average flowering season of more than five months. The *Quintral* (see page 62) blossoms from January to May, and as a hemiparasite, it depends on the abundance and resistance of the trees where it grows. They are distributed in *Argentina* from *Neuquén* to *Chubut*. In the winter, the populations of Green-backed Firecrown feed exclusively on the flowers of the *Quintral*.

The Firebush and the native *Fuchsia* (see page 59), among others, are also pollinated by the hummer.

The forest and the flowers

In the *Lanín* and *Nahuel Huapí* National Parks there are plants which flower every month of the year, with a maximum between mid-November and the beginning of December.

As we travel south towards *Tierra del Fuego*, or the higher grounds above sea level, the formation of the buds and flowering come later.

Flowering Ages

Years	
less than 10	Firebush, Winter's bark, Fuinque, Avellano.
10 to 20	Maitén, Roble Pellín.
20 to 40	*Nothofagus sp.,* Alerce, Maniú hembra.
40 to 60	*Araucaria.*

The temptation of the fruits

Evolution must have moulded two tendencies in the spreading of seeds from the plants:

• Little investment in each seed and fruit, but with massive production. The wind is the main transporter.

• Great investment in the quality of seed and fruit, but with limited production. With relations of mutual benefit surged by coevolution, the animals are the main spreaders.

"Gone with the wind"
Second Part

Species of the forest that depend on the wind for the spreading of their seeds tend to have brief periods of unripe fruits. The seeds will be dispersed before the coming of winter.

If there is no wind, the seeds fall to the ground by gravity at a distance once or twice the height of the tree. This is the case of the conifers. Great changes in ground level or water courses may represent an additional help.
There are notable differences in the production of seeds. For the *Coihue* (data from the area of *Valdivia, Chile*) the number of seeds varied from 9 million to almost 170 million units per hectare.

Fleshy fruit

"He who eats the calafate comes back for more"

This tempting and gastronomic patagonian phrase makes reference to a fleshy, violet coloured, almost 1 cm. in diameter and small seeded fruit.

Who in the wildlife are receivers of such desired fruit? Well, those animals willing to transport their seeds. This means that the fruit must include not only a good amount of nutrients (sugar, protein, fat), they must come in attractive containers, and be accessible to the spreaders.

In our Southern Beech Forests many bushes have fleshy fruit. They are mainly small, red or black and have 1 to 3 seeds, as you can prove by simple observation. Their appearance is less seasonal than the flowering, and their variation in production and viability is greater than in flowers. Partly because of the major dependence that fruit have on resources and pollinators.

To reduce the risk of drying up or being destroyed, it favours them to be eaten soon after maturing. In the Southern Forests many fleshy fruit mature towards the end of summer, period in which many birds, mostly

Tactics of seed dispersal

Length or maximum diameter of seeds and fruits in milimeters (mm)

Dry fruits

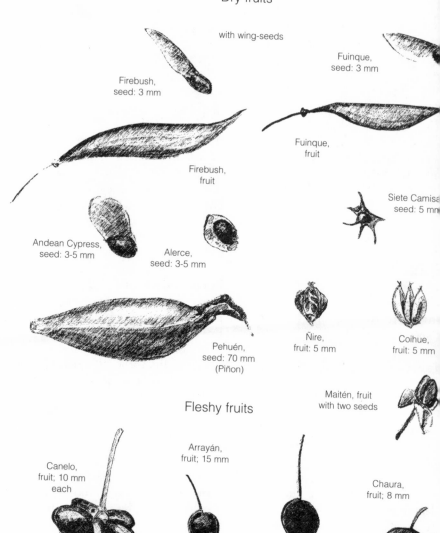

with wing-seeds

Firebush,
seed: 3 mm

Fuinque,
seed: 3 mm

Firebush,
fruit

Fuinque,
fruit

Siete Camisa
seed: 5 mm

Andean Cypress,
seed: 3-5 mm

Alerce,
seed: 3-5 mm

Pehuén,
seed: 70 mm
(Piñon)

Ñire,
fruit: 5 mm

Coihue,
fruit: 5 mm

Fleshy fruits

Maitén, fruit
with two seeds

Canelo,
fruit; 10 mm
each

Arrayán,
fruit; 15 mm

Chaura,
fruit; 8 mm

Calafate,
fruit; 10 mm

migrating ones, eat more to store reserves.

On the other hand, in mid-summer here is an abundance of insects, nutritive pieces that the birds need especially to feed their chicks.

Very few fleshy fruit plants mature in winter. Among them the Chaura (see page 60) and the creeper Estrellita. During the cold season, insects are scarce; therefore there is less predation of seeds. But there are less dispersers available. As a strategy, these plants make their fruit mature in stages. They allow more time for their few clients to take what they offer. On the other hand, the fleshy fruit in winter generally have less pulp and lower nutritive value. Having less competition, they don't receive a good selective pressure to produce more.

Once a seed falls to the ground, its new target is to establish itself and survive. Waiting is an alternative of adaptation to an uncertain environment: seeds can be in lethargy and if conditions are good, germinate.

Bushes in peat bog areas (see page 64) offer fleshy fruit in summer. The geese can make nests in the peat bog areas and eat the red fruit of the Murtilla, a shrubby bush. Some bushes in this environment hold their fruit even in winter up till spring, offering fruit when it is scarce.

What similarities are there between the care of the embryo in mammals and the plants with fruit?

They have been compared, considering they have a mother that supplies nutrients and protection. In this way, the new generation comes to the world with higher development, and in consequence with more chances to survive.

The growth and death of trees

There are plants that grow quickly and others very slowly. Different variables have to be considered. The tree species that grow the fastest produce shade and don't allow other species to get enough direct sunlight energy. Water and nutrients are other basic requirements.

The number of saplings is really high (pioneer species; see page 14) Coihues that are less than a mete tall can have a density of 40,000 individuals per hectare. For the Lenga and Guindo it is known that they may have densities of ove 100,000 young plants per hectare!

In mature forests in *Tierra del Fuego* the *Guindo* saplings may persist 50 t 100 years for a clearing that allow light to get through. The *Lenga* tend to resist less but its abundant shoot will grow rapidly if the falling o trees creates a clearing.

Trees can break or be uprooted b the strong winds (especially ir areas with not very deep soils). The intertwining of roots betweer neighbouring trees helps to holc them up. In *Tierra del Fuego*, almos 90 % of the uprooting is caused b the wind. Clear examples are observed near the coast from the Beagle Channel, where the influence of sea environment must be added The snow avalanches may b another devastating effect on the *Nothofagus* forest.

Fallen branches and trunks will las for decades before they disappear. Ir *Tierra del Fuego*, big branches from

Alerce

the *Lenga* will take over 50 years to decompose, and it is estimated that 500 years should go by before a fallen trunk loses 99 % of its mass.

An abundance of logs, still standing or lying down may give a first impression of an unhealthy forest. But appearances may be tricky. Plants and fungi colonise them and diverse insects live in their wood. The Magellan Woodpecker (see page 75) usually makes its nest in holes of logs that are still standing, and diverse birds of prey (like the Bicoloured Hawk) make them in trunks of lifeless trees. From there they have clear (and probably spectacular) views, to detect possible preys (there is no proof to know if· they enjoy the view...). Owls like the Austral Pigmy Owl (see page 86) and the Great Horned Owl, also have relation with this environment. We can say that these birds, in a way, depend on the dead trees.

Among mammals, the Red Fox may have its young in the hollows of trees, and on the coasts of many lakes in the *Nahuel Huapi* National Park, the fallen trees favour the Large River Otter to make its burrows (see page 99).

The accumulation of leaves, twigs, flowers, fruits and cones on the ground as a general tendency increases from *Neuquén* to *Tierra del Fuego*, as with lower temperatures decreases the decomposition rates.

Lenga

In your walks along different latitudes of our forests you will realise the difference.

But also things change according to the dominating trees: for example, the decomposition in a forest of *alerces* (see page 49) is not the same as in a *Lenga* forest (see page 52).

Pure or mixed forests

The climate and soil limit the development of diversity in the forest. The practically pure *Lenga* forests occupy a good part of the forest area in the region. The pure forests of *Alerce*, *Araucaria* and Andean Cypress are related to the type of soil.

Pioneer species (see page 14) also form pure areas with new shoots. For example, the Coihue Southern Beech, the *Roble Pellín*, the Winter's bark or the Firebush.

The winds or the action of pests and plagues may enhance the massive damage to pure forests. The risks are greater for the monoculture of forest trees (even more if there is no good management) as with the *Monterrey* Pine, native from California (see page 105).

On the other hand, the mixed forests protect the river basins or streams in an effective way, as the roots of different trees reach different depths and retain the water better.

In our Valdivian Forest, there are from 10 to 15 different species of trees per hectare, while in all our fuegian forest there are only 5 or 6 tree species. In comparison, up to 45 species per hectare grow in the Misiones Subtropical Rainforest and over 300 species per hectare in the diverse Amazon Rainforest.

Andean Cypress

Resistance and Adaptation

Lack of water

Scarce rainfall, intense winds, winter frosts (sometimes in spring and even in summer) occur in different habitats of our forests. The summers are relatively dry while precipitation concentrates mainly in the cold months.

It mustn't seem strange that even though certain areas receive a lot of water and snow every year (over 3,500 mm. in the dampest section of our Valdivian Forest), the leaves of many species of trees are adapted to conditions of frequent droughts.

They are small, hard and coriaceous. The cuticle has a layer of wax that helps regulate the evaporation. But with strong winds, this may not be enough. Therefore, there are other adaptations.

The leaves of the *Coihue* have a lot of stoma (pores where gases are interchanged), but if there is a lack of water they close. However, this species has on its leaves microscopic hairs (trichomes) that secrete volatile components that act as thermal isolators (terpenes that help to resist freezing). Also, the constant evaporation contributes to diminish the loss of water by transpiration.

The stoma of the *Firebush* (see page 59) leaves in comparison, are just a few. This may be because the mature plant can't close them completely

Cohiue

(this means the risk of loss would be greater). For the species that lose their leaves seasonally, to cause an early shedding is an adaptation to droughts.

Low temperature

The evergreen trees of our forests are less adapted to the cold than those in the Northern Hemisphere. The dominance of oceans in the southern half of the world determines that the changes in temperature between winter and summer are more moderate. That is why if occasionally there are sudden drastic changes; the risk of suffering consequences is greater.

While the seasons go by, the plants adapt themselves to the climate. Leaves and stems of woody species are more resistant to the cold in winter than the end of spring or summer.

Among the *Nothofagus*, the *Ñire* and the *Lenga* are more resistant to the low temperatures, and the loss of leaves helps them. The *Coihue* is also very resistant to cold, but doesn't shed its leaves seasonally. This species contains certain aminoacids and proteins whose concentration increase at lower temperatures. They could give certain protection against freezing (substances with this function are known in diverse organisms, as some macroalgae, antarctic fishes, and bees).

On the other hand, it is proved that in winter the leaves of the *Coihue* have more chloroplast (organelles with chlorophyll for photosynthesis) per cell in summer, being this a possible adaptation to the decrease of intensity and hours of daylight.

Towards colder habitats, species like the Firebush, the *Fuinque* and the *Avellano*, partially lose their leaves and buds, while their stems resist. Because of their low content of water (less risk of freezing) and almost nil metabolism, the mature seeds of these plants are also resistant.

Fire, volcanoes and earthquakes

Natural causes or the direct or indirect action of human provoque fires of variable magnitude in the forest.

The electric storms are one of the natural causes, more probable in the *Nahuel Huapi* and *Lanin* National Parks latitudes, and almost absent in *Tierra del Fuego*.

Between 1938 and 1982, the lightning may have originated 15 % of the fires of known causes between the north of *Lanín* National Park and the south of *Los Alerces* National Park, according to the registers of the National Park Administration.

After several seasons of drought, the accumulation of flammable material raise the probability for fires and the effect of *La Niña* has influenced in this sense in the last years.

The first aborigine groups in this area used fire to communicate, hunt, cook, or just to keep warm. The brave *mapuches* used it as defence when attacking. Jesuits and pioneer explorers wrote down their observations over vast areas of burnt forests in the southern area of *Neuquén* and northern *Río Negro*. After the campaigns against aborigines (1879-1883), the fires became less frequent.

During the colonisation the fires were really immense. At the beginning of the 20th century, 300,000 hectares of forests between *Neuquén* and *Río Negro* were eliminated to be replace by cattle rising. Years after that, fires diminished and the Andean Cypress spread in that habitat. However, it has been suggested that this spreading may have been caused by climatic changes. By 1915, after several years of drought, 38 % of the forests of *Neuquén* and *Río Negro* had burnt.

In *Santa Cruz* the forests are less extense. They suffered intense fires from 1915 to 1950 and almost all the present forests of *Ñire* may be recovery forests. In this territory, the *Lenga* and *Guindo* grow preferably towards the more protected andean valleys. In *Tierra del Fuego*, the fires also were important in the past, but in the last decades they have been scarce.

Changes in climate with a tendency of decrease in annual rainfall of up to 30 % have been registered for three decades in *Chubut* and *Santa Cruz*. But it rains the same or more than normal in the area of Neuquén and *Río Negro*. In spite of this, the great fires in the last seasons are taking place in these provinces, especially in *Río Negro*.

There are plants with several adaptations to fire. The *Araucaria* (see page 49) grows in relatively dry habitats and areas of volcanic eruptions (more frequent in past centuries) where the risk of fire is great. Its thick, dense and not very flammable bark, would be a protective adaptation. Its branches grow at a considerable height, more protected from the flames. Also the protected buds may grow after the fire, although the young ones die.

Some species have resistant seeds and

Pehuén

fires stimulate their germination. But the introduction of cattle to burnt areas causes great death among the saplings plants. The *Nothofagus* aren't resistant to fire but have a great capacity as colonizers.

The volcanoes let out immense quantity of ash that may cover all the vegetation. Such was the case of the Hudson volcano (Chilean) that

37

erupted the last time in 1991. Still half buried in ash, the Ñire produces adventitious roots from the base of its branches to survive. Lengas buried up to a meter or more can develop a lateral system of roots closer to the ground level, and the Coihue does similarly. The *Chusquea* canes (as the *Coihue*, see page 58) develop their strength after a fire and can stop the growth of trees. But if the debris and ash cover them, in general, the regeneration of trees is more probable.

The tremors can also affect the growth of trees, or even kill them damaging their roots. In 1949, for example, a number of falls of *Nothofagus* was registered in certain areas of *Tierra del Fuego*. An earthquake with epicentre close to Lake *Fagnano* was declared guilty, and the floods created were also an indirect consequence.

In places close to *Lago Traful*, *Nahuel Huapi* National Park, you can see *Coihue* and Andean Cypress with narrow growth rings (indicator of scarce development) corresponding to the years 1737, 1751, 1837 and 1960. Earthquakes were registered in that area in those years.

As regards fauna, in 1960 a seismic movement was registered in the area of *Lago Nahuel Huapi* and produced the decrease in number of the nesting Imperial Cormorant colony in the lake, one of the few non sea-coast populations of the species.

Ice: Past and Present

Aproximate ice limits, 20.000 years ago
(last glacial maximum)

Past ...

Can you imagine marine waters up to
120 meters below their actual levels,
and 40 % more emerged lands in the
world than now?

These were some of the consequences
of the Pleistocene glaciations (2
millions to 18,000 years ago) at their
maximum level. In these circum-
stances, through immense land
bridges, North America (via Alaska)

had period of connection with *Siberia* (this bridge reached 90 km from west to east and 900 km. from north to south); England to Europe; Sicily to Italy; New Guinea to Australia and the latter to Antarctica; and in our area, *Tierra del Fuego* to Continental *Patagonia*. Water started to run again between the extremes of the Magellan Strait 9,000 years ago.

Close to twenty glaciations occurred in the world during the Pleistocene, each one with an average length of 100,000 years, separated close to 10,000 years one from the other. In periods of maximum defrosting, the sea level got to be above the present one. The largest expansion of ice occurred around one million years ago. In areas south of the *Gallegos* River the advances of ice got to the Atlantic coast. The last global glaciations started 70,000 years ago, and in *Patagonia* the last glaciation advance occurred 14,500 years ago.

Ice has moulded the land with great strength. We can see their work of impressing dimension in the U-shaped valleys in all the Andean *Patagonia*, or in the Beagle Channel in *Tierra del Fuego*.

In *Santa Cruz* province the surface of *Los Glaciares* National Park was completely covered by ice, in certain areas reaching a thickness of 900 to 1,400 meters. Four main glacial advances were detected, and in the largest, they reached up to 80 km to the east of *Lago Argentino*.

With so much ice, the seas had less water. Therefore, the evaporation decreased and at global level, the climate was drier and colder, and the winds were stronger. The barren lands and the change of sea level may have had a great influence over the forms of life. In South America, during the Pleistocene, 80 % of the genus of great land mammals disappeared (as *Mylodon*, *Glyptodon*, *Toxodon*, etc.). Also, the presence of human hunters in those last stages may have influenced the extinctions in such short time.

After the Patagonian ice retreated, great basins and glacial moraines remained (sediments transported by the moving ice). Countless lakes (see page 44) appeared, being dominant with a west-east orientation.

The almost uniform forests of *Nothofagus* in *Tierra del Fuego* and south of *Patagonia* suggest that a small amount of vegetation survived the glaciers advanced. After their retreating, the forests were able to recolonise.

...Present

The so called Continental Icefield is the most visible remains of the glaciations. They represent the most important amount of ice in the Southern Hemisphere, after Antarctica.

When they encounter the mountains the Pacific winds loaded with water, rise and condense, therefore producing snowfalls that amount to over 6000 mm annually in this region.

Among the glaciers in the world, the Patagonian ones are found in the most temperate climate, and most of them are retreating.

The North Patagonian Icefield, in Chile, reaches around 4,200 km^2. The *San Rafael* Glacier, one of the two greatest in the sector, has retreated an average of 190 to 300 meters annually from 1985 to 1990. Its front descends to the waters of the *San Rafael* Lake. Connected to the sea waters of the Chilean fjords, it receives tide influence.

The South Patagonian Icefield has a surface of 14,000 km^2 and 350 km of extension from north to south. With a maximum width of 90 km in the north sector, it narrows southwards till it disappears in the chileans *Bernardo O'Higgins* and *Torres del Paine* National Park.

In *Argentina*, *Los Glaciares* National Park includes 2600 km^2 in that sector, with 13 great glaciers that descend to the basins of the *Lago Argentino* and *Lago Viedma*. Among them the largest are the *Upsala* (595 km^2) and *Viedma* (575 km^2).

The *Upsala* is approximately 60 km long and 4 km wide near its front. It is considered to be the largest glacier in South America. Between 1970 and 1978 its eastern side advanced 400 meters while its western side suffered a small retreat. It retreated the following years, and between 1981 and 1984 it had more than 2 km of break-offs in the eastern margin. Since then until 1990, recesses have been recorded of up to 200 meters annually. The *Viedma* Glacier has had fewer variations.

The *Perito Moreno* Glacier with 250 km^2 flows to the *Brazo Rico*, tributary of the *Lago Argentino*. It is a tongue of ice almost 30 km long which descends trapped by mounts. It ranges from 2,000 meters to 180 meters above sea level, with an impressive and irregular front rising between 50 and 60 meters.

The registers show that in 1900 the front started to cross the *Brazo Rico* of *Lago Argentino*. In 1917 the glacier arrives to the opposite *Peninsula de Magallanes* coast forming a small dam. Since then the erosive action of the water broke the ice walls once and again. The last rupture occurred in February 1988. Since then, the ice has not yet reached the opposite coast of the channel, and has not formed a dam that lasts.

The glaciologists consider that the glacier is stable.

The *survival of the fittest* is a metaphor known by almost everyone. It may convey a confuse perspective over the concept of competition in Nature. We can associate it to cruel battles among organisms. A fight between the weak and the strong.

However, in some areas, it seems that the environmental conditions and not the competition between organisms are the main determinant in survival. In the forest, the living beings must put up with cold and snow, the risk of dying out, fire, volcanoes and earthquakes, and till not so long ago, the great advance and recess of ice.

This is how the Russian born Petr Kropotkin interpreted it after years of observation and perception of his world: the rigorous Siberia.

Darwin and Wallace, who conceived the concept of evolution of the species almost simultaneously, had their main experiences in other latitudes. Many of their experiences occurred in tropical or temperate environments with great diversity in forms of life.

In the cold *Siberia*, the competition between organisms doesn't seem to rule the relations of living beings with the struggle for survival.
Kropotkin concluded that under severe environmental conditions, the cooperation was the dominant strategy.

Competition and cooperation: in these pages there are examples of one and the other in the natural world.

In 1902 Kropotkin published *Mutual aid: a factor of Evolution*. Did it deal with Nature? Yes, and with many examples.
But he also associated it to society. He was an anarchist, and his work contrasted with the Darwinian vision held by the British.

The biologist Stephen Jay Gould, considered that both viewpoints were wrong in trying to apply the concepts of natural evolution to society. It is neither worth the time nor the space to try to justify why, but I believe it is worth mentioning that the rules of the game between one and the other reality are totally different. Some examples may be useful. Eagles represent to man, power, dominance, competitiveness and freedom. It's that they are really impressive. There are firms and nations that have them as an emblem. USA chose the Bald Eagle as national bird. By the way, this eagle, mostly a fisher, is also a scavenger. A convenient strategy in the natural world.

As counterpart to the symbolism we give, many species of big eagles in the world are in danger of becoming extinct.

In history there are remarkable facts of wrong conclusions and theories. But science continuously seeks to find "the truth", testing, willingly or not, the truth.

The Lakes and the Forest

There are more than 160 lakes that can be considered of a certain importance in the Andean-Patagonian region. The vastest being *Lago Buenos Aires* (*Santa Cruz*) that is 2,200 km² including the Chilean portion. Of the ones completely in *Argentina*, the largest is *Lago Argentino*, 1,415 km².

Their shapes are more irregular towards the west, while lateral and terminal moraines limit them towards the east. The main Patagonian rivers that flow towards the Atlantic are born in these lakes, although some basins drain towards the Pacific.

Galaxias sp.

They may be seen as islands (see page 5): water surrounded by land instead of land surrounded by water. The aquatic fauna in general is not very diverse, although in less deep lakes their abundance may be greater. It may be more isolated in the "aquatic islands" and in these conditions they are more liable to changes. Such as the ones produced by the construction of dams in rivers that communicate water basins, or by the introduced species of fish (see page 103).

The Puyenes (*Galaxias* genus; present also in New Zealand), the *Pejerrey Patagónico*, the *Perca* or *Trucha Criolla*, the *Bagre Aterciopelado* and the *Bagre de los Torrentes* are some of the native fish. The insularity can be also a problem for the *Huillín* (Large River Otter; see page 99), of the Mustelidae family.

Let's consider now the trees that grow near our Andean lakes. The Conifers, rich in tannin and resins, are scarce, except for the Andean Cypress in some areas. The *Nothofagus* forests are dominant, with species that don't produce many dead leaves and don't have tannin and resins. They also have a system of roots that are an efficient barrier to slow down the washing away of nutrients in the soil towards the lakes. This is valid especially between *Neuquén* and *Chubut* and in *Tierra del*

Fuego, as in *Santa Cruz* the main body of the lakes are generally found in steppe environments.

In contrast, the conifers dominate around lakes in northern North America, and around many European lakes. Their tannin darkens the water in those latitudes.

And...?

Let's dive in a quiet and peaceful north Patagonian lake with transparent waters (no excuses, even though you are cold). The light can get through, but the microalgae (phytoplankton) have low concentration there, partly for the lack of nitrogen. The light doesn't allow the growth of the cyanobacteria, micro-organisms that retain the nitrogen from the air. If the cyanobacteria were present they would collaborate with the supply of nitrogen for the microalgae.

And...?

The fact is that the monoculture of conifers (especially in *Chile*, because of their largest extension) takes more tannin to the water, and in consequence makes them darker. This means that less light can penetrate, therefore the cyanobacteria can proliferate and hence favour the development of phytoplankton, and ..., and...

Conclusion: Great changes in the dynamics of water life in the lakes can be produced as a consequence of the extensive pines plantations.

Along the paths of the Forest (III)

Trees

Outstanding species of trees with their coverage percentage in the Patagonian Forests in Argentina (according to Laclau, 1997)

Lenga 52%

Coihue 6%

Roble Pellín and Raulí 2%

Pehuén 4%

Others: 5%

Andean Cypress 3%

Ñire 28%

Where are them?: The map on color page I shows the distribution area.

The appearance of wood

In the Plant Kingdom the appearance of wood would be the result of evolutionary processes determined by natural selection. The tendency went towards the elaboration of components whose functions were support and resistance. The majority of animals can't digest wood, which also has a low nutritive value. We also can consider the chitin of the crabs, substance present in their shell, the hair of mammals, and feathers on birds to be similar components. Their function may be structural (*chitin*), protection and isolation (hair), or everything (*chitin*).

On the following pages I mention only a few common and representative species from over fifty tree species in the Southern Forests.

The size of the trees in the forests

Guiding values of height and diameter (in meters), valid for *Argentina* (in *Chile* they are usually taller and wider). Values that aren't available, or whose variation is not representative are indicated with an "x". The trees that are illustrated are drawn in scale according to their maximum height.

The data indicated is: maximum height - frequent height/ maximum diameter - frequent diameter. Example: *Pehuén* 40-25/ 2-1.

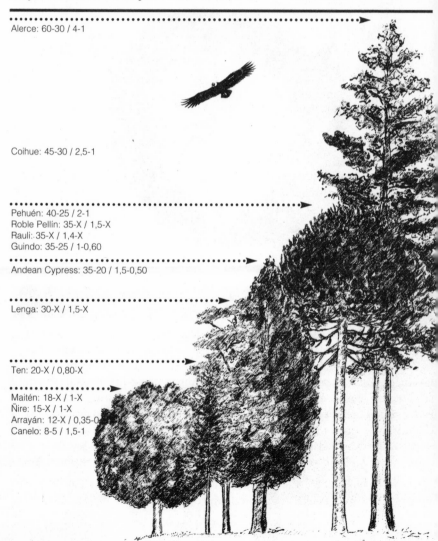

Alerce: 60-30 / 4-1

Coihue: 45-30 / 2,5-1

Pehuén: 40-25 / 2-1
Roble Pellín: 35-X / 1,5-X
Rauli: 35-X / 1,4-X
Guindo: 35-25 / 1-0,60

Andean Cypress: 35-20 / 1,5-0,50

Lenga: 30-X / 1,5-X

Ten: 20-X / 0,80-X

Maitén: 18-X / 1-X
Ñire: 15-X / 1-X
Arrayán: 12-X / 0,35-0
Canelo: 8-5 / 1,5-1

The Conifers:

Nine species of conifers grow in our Southern Beech Forests. The pollination (see page 25) and dispersion of their seeds depends mainly on the wind (see page 29).

The Pehuén

It grows in *Argentina* only in the province of *Neuquén*. It prefers rocky and sandy grounds, generally of volcanic origin and over 800 m above sea level.

It has a slow development and there are trees over 1,000 years old. It is considered a relict species (see page 13) and it is said that it is retreating because of the advance of arid lands due to climatic changes. It forms pure forests (see page 34) or community assemblages with *Lenga*, *Coihue* or *Ñire*.

Its leaves are strong and coriaceous (see page 23). The bark from 10 to 15 cm thick (see page 37) is rugged and a resin protects it from insects.

The *Pehuén* produces male and female (larger) cones and they mature in August.

After fecundation, the feminine cones harden (lignify) with approximately 200 seeds inside. The pines open over a year later in autumn. The wingless seeds that weigh three to four grams fall to the ground a short distance away. Rodents and birds like the Chilean Pigeon and the Austral Parakeet (see page 80) help to spread them. In areas of the Valdivian Forest in *Chile* we also find the Slender-billed *Conure* (Psittacidae family). Its peculiar beak, very hook-like, is a good adaptation to open the pinecones.

These animals might also cause certain degree of predation and there are rodents that store the pinecones to provide in periods of scarcity. The seeds have a high nutritive value and have been very important in the diet of the Mapuches.

The Alerce

The *Alerce* trees in *Los Alerces* National Park form a forest of giants. They can also be found in *Puerto Blest* and *Laguna Frias* (*Nahuel Huapi* National Park), among others places. In *Chile*, the area of distribution is more ample, however reduced in relation to the surface covered before the colonisation.

It grows on poor soil permanently damp and a bit swampy, and needs good light. It is considered relict species (see page 13).

With individuals that are registered to be 3,600 years old (the oldest tree in *Los Alerces* National Park called "*El Abuelo*" -The Grandfather-, is close to 2,600 years old), this tree species is the third older in the world. It grows very slowly, with values of about one mm in diameter per year.

In young *alerces* with good access to light, the branches grow close to the ground. However in the forest, you can only observe alerces with high branches. The leaves are small and slim and resemble scales. Under the bark they have fibre layers full of resin, and the wood is not easily attacked by insects.

The seeds possess two or three wings and the wind spreads them in autumn. In years of high production the viability of the seeds is also greater (up to 12.5 % according to observable data).

Clearings in the forest and soil with dead leaves favour the seeds as they can receive more intensity of light and have higher humidity. Decomposing big fallen logs are also a good place for the seeds to start growing.

The Andean Cypress

They are distributed between *Neuquén* and *Chubut*, from 700 to 1,500 meters above sea level. They form pure forests towards the zone of transition with the steppe, on poor eroded soil many times of volcanic origin. The low temperatures affect them and snow can damage the small plants. They are frequently found close to river courses and lakes. Also they colonise unlevelled ground. Towards the steppes the high evaporation is a limiting factor for their development. In mixed forests they grow close to other species like the Winter's bark, *Coihue* and *Alerce*. In *Argentina*, they cover a total of approximately 159,000 hectares.

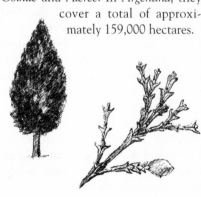

They can live around 1,000 years, but the majority of specimens are much younger. The existence of only few older trees is related with fires (see page 37) and the forest exploitation in the past. They do not reproduce in vegetative form and the bark is very thin, therefore very sensitive to fire. However, after fires they can regenerate well. Cattle breeding may result in the deformation of future trunks.

The roots of this species may extend thirty meters away from the trunk, allowing a great grip on the ground, being able to resist the winds. But their form and strength are affected by very strong winds.

In isolated individuals the branches may grow even from the trunk base, but in dense forests they grow higher up. They have thin leaves, scaly like the ones of the *Alerce*, and rather soft. When the small fruit matures in summer they open and the winged seeds are liberated. They are almost all spread in a week (it is known that the majority of species take one to four months to do this). Different insects like caterpillars, predate them.

and damp soils. In *Chile* it grows up to *Tierra del Fuego* being the southernmost conifer in the world. In *Argentina* it is less frequent; to the north you can find it in the zone of Puerto Blest (*Nahuel Huapi* National Park), in to the south in areas as *Lago Roca* (*Los Glaciares* National Park), where it grows near the peat bogs dominated by *Sphagnum* moss. It has a hard and thin bark and the leaves are small. They produce winged seeds.

• • •

The *Ciprés* de las Guaytecas

The *Ciprés* de las *Guaytecas*, or *Ten*, belong to the same family of the *Alerce* (see page 49). It prefers swampy

The flowering trees

The *Nothofagus*

The trees of the *Nothofagus* genus

include forty living species. Nine of them grow in the Southern Beech Forests in *Argentina* and *Chile*, and thirty one in Australasia (see page 18). Fossils of another forty species are also known. Some of them from the Peninsula Antarctica (there are even some 400 km from the South Pole) and Tasmania.

When the Continental masses were united, the *Nothofagus* had the chance of extending their distribution. But it is not clear where they originated and which were their migration routes. However it seems that they neither reach Africa nor India.

Catastrophes are important in the regeneration of the *Nothofagus* in our region. In general they don't tolerate shade and their saplings need big clearings to develop.

Volcanic activity and earthquakes (see page 38) aren't rare in various areas of the Andean forests. Some *Nothofagus* species are the first to establish and dominate devastated areas (the mycorrhiza help; see page 67). Slow growing species that are more tolerant to shade may replace them.

They depend on the wind for their pollination (see page 25). They tend to produce seeds massively and the wind (see page 29) is the most important agent of dispersion. The *Nothofagus* can cover the ground with seeds, but there are also bad years. They require a period of recovery to accumulate sufficient reserves before they can have another year of high productivity. On these occasions, the percentage of viability of the seeds is also greater.

Fungi (like the *Llao-llao*, among the ones you can find and recognise more easily; see page 68) and hemiparasite plants (see page 62) affect them. Various epiphytes (see page 61) grow on their trunks and branches.

Forests of *Nothofagus* with big trunks (fallen or not) in slow decomposition, are the habitat required by some species of birds (see page 32).

Nothofagus species (distribution map, page 15) in *Argentina* are:

The Lenga

Length: 2 - 4 cm

It's the tree that covers the greatest surface in our Andean-Patagonian Forests. The area of the lakes of Epulaufquen in Neuquén province is the northern limit of distribution in the country. From there with some interruptions it grows as far as Tierra del Fuego. It requires low temperatures

The reproductive cycle of the trees

The Nothofagus (flowers of separate sex on the same tree):
In Autumn, the buds of flowers are formed.
In Spring, flowers are pollinated.
End of spring, seeds mature and wind spreads them.
The Andean Cypress and the Alerce also have a yearly reproductive cycle.
The Pehuén, Avellano and Ulmo need two years.

for its development. Their lifespan is about 300 years.

Above sea level grows close to 1,800 m in Neuquén and to 600 m in Tierra del Fuego, delimiting the timberline in mountain slopes (see page 21).

As you climb up the Patagonian mountains slopes you may find pure forests of Lenga. At lower altitudes they form mixed forests with the Coihue, Pehuén and Raulí. And in Tierra del Fuego they can be found with the Guindo close to the sea shore. It sheds its leaves in autumn (see page 24).

Where there are Chusquea canes (see page 58) the Lenga saplings may be dormant for some years till a clearing is formed, allowing the light it needs to grow. They are sensitive to the attack of certain insects (see page 70).

The Ñire

Length: 0,6 - 3 cm

The Ñire is distributed from Neuquén to Tierra del Fuego. It is a species that has adapted itself to grow under variable conditions. From areas with

53

bad drainage close to peat bogs (see page 64) to steep mountain slopes exposed to winds. They also resist low temperatures. Its morphology vary from small trees to shrubby bushes.

The grey bark is cracked. In autumn the leaves go reddish (see page 24) before they fall. In many trees has been observed partial death of the crown, especially in the areas of transition with the steppe. The age would be the main cause for this. It lives over 200 years.

The Coihue

Length: 2 - 4 cm

It grows in the Valdivian Forest and gets close to 1,000 m over sea level on the Andean mountain slopes. It prefers damp soils.

It is the tallest species among our *Nothofagus*. The oldest individuals are 500 to 600 years old. The bark presents shallow cracks which are a good support for epiphytes (see page 61) as you may observe.

It's an evergreen species and the leaves are adapted to the lack of water and cold temperatures (see page 35). It requires good light growing rapidly in open areas. Great fallen logs that stand over the level of shade of the canes, may be a good place to grow.

The *Coihue* form pure forests and mixed ones. For example with the *Roble Pellín* in damp areas, with the *Lenga* in more elevated areas, or with the Austral Cypress in lower and less rainy places. The *Chusquea* canes forms dense cane thickets under the *Coihue* forest (see page 58).

The Guindo or Coihue de Magallanes

Length: 0,5 - 2,5 cm

It replaces the *Coihue* in the Austral or Magellan Forest. The western area of *Lago Azara* (*Santa Cruz*) is the northern boundary of distribution. Southwards it grows up to *Tierra del Fuego* and Staten Island, preferably in humid areas. It can live up to 500 years. It is an evergreen and the leaves are coriaceous (see page 35).

In its distribution area there are many retreating glaciers (see page 40) leaving exposed moraines. There lack of nitrogen is one of the main imitations for plants growing, and he *Guindo* is one of the first colonisers. Evergreen species are more tolerant to these conditions, and on the other hand the *Coihue* roots are associated to bacteria and fungi that hold nitrogen ("mycorrhiza", see page 67).

In the chilean *Torres del Paine* National Park it has been proved that in moraine areas the *Guindo*, and also the *Ñire*, have a growth rate up to three times greater than the *Lenga*.

The Raulí

Length: 7 - 12 cm

In *Argentina* it only grows in limited areas of the *Lanín* National Park (for example on mountain slopes around *Lacar*, *Lolog*, *Huechulaufquen* and *Paimún* lakes).

It can grow at a height of 1,300 m above sea level on the mountain slopes and usually is associated to the *Coihue* and *Roble Pellín*. It prefers fertile deep and humid soils. It sheds its leaves in autumn. These get to be 12 cm long, 4 cm wide (even bigger in *Chile*), the greatest in size among the *Nothofagus* in *Argentina*.

The Roble Pellín

Length: 2 - 5 cm

In Argentina, its main forests grow only in restricted areas in Lanín National Park and you find it also, for example, in areas of lago Epulaufquen, Neuquén.

Among the Nothofagus, it is the species whose distribution is the farthest to the north. In Chile it appears at latitude close to the one of Santiago de Chile, being a remnant of a flora that colonised those areas during the glaciations.

The Arrayán

Los Arrayanes National Park (Peninsula *Quetrihué*, *Nahuel Huap* National Park) protects a dense forest of this species, including huge trees. *Quetri* means arrayán in *Araucano* and *Quetrihué*, place of *arrayanes*.

The Winter's bark (canelo)

It's a myrtle that grows in various areas of the Valdivian Forest, preferably close to water courses. The shapes can vary between trees with twisted branches to bushy ones. It has a slow development.

It is easy to identify by its smooth reddish peeling bark with white spots that correspond to the fall of plaques of the bark. Why is it difficult to find epiphytes on these trees? Surely shedding of the bark is responsible (see page 61).

The leaves of the *Arrayán* are evergreen and aromatic. The white flowers are hermaphrodite and after pollination, they give black rounded berry fruit that are 1,5 cm in diameter and have three small seeds. Certain birds and mammals help with their dispersal (see page 81).

This species is distributed in Central and South America, present in the Patagonian forest from *Neuquén* to *Tierra del Fuego* and Staten Island. They belong to the Winteraceae, and antique family.

The *Canelo* grows in swampy areas and close to water courses, both in shade and under direct sunlight. It's an evergreen species with big leaves, smooth edges, relatively disorganised veins and irregular branching. Although being a flowering plant, its trunk has tracheids like the conifers instead of vessels to transport the sap, a slower and more inefficient system.

The features of its leaves and the racheids are primitive ones.

The bark contains tannin, essential oils and antibacterial substances. The flowers are white and hermaphrodite, but the pollen can't fertilise the ovule of the same flower. It flowers in spring and insects take part in the pollination (see page 27). It gives small black berries that ripe between December and March. Birds act as seeds dispersers. Contrasting with the *Nothofagus* for example, high percentage of its seeds are viable (70 % to 100 %).

The Maitén

It grows in areas of transition between the forest and the steppe, from *Neuquén* to *Chubut*. It forms small pure forests in various places, however, they grow disperse. The branches are thin, long and hang down. It's an evergreen species of dense foliage, with leaves of variable shape and size, and coriaceous (leather like) consistency.

The same tree gives masculine, feminine and hermaphrodite flowers. It flowers in August and September, and its fruit are coriaceous capsules with two fleshy red covered seeds. Birds help with their dispersion. The *Quintral* (see page 62) is frequently over the *Maitén*.

•••

Growing under the trees: the understory

The canes dominate in the humid and shade strata of bushes and herbs that grow under the trees of the dense Valdivian Forest. Bushes that require more light grow in clearings or borders, as the Firebush, the *Chilco* and the *Chaura*. You can find them frequently at the sides of roads. The *Nalca* with huge leaves and noticeable inflorescences grows close to water courses where there is high humidity, places also convenient for ferns.

In *Santa Cruz* and *Tierra del Fuego*, the understory is quite open and the forest in general it is easier to explore. The canes don't get there. Although in *Tierra del Fuego* bushes like the *Michay* (see page 60) that have long stems and prickly leaves, may be difficult to transit.

Some common species of the understory easily identified and representative for their abundance are:

The Colihue cane

The *Chusquea* is the most diverse genus of canes in America (see page 16), with more than ninety species from Mexico (including the Caribbean Islands) to the Andean Patagonian region. Among them the *Colihue* cane is present in the Valdivian Forest growing as far south as *Lago Buenos Aires* (north of *Santa Cruz* province).

The *Colihue* is solid and may grow over five meters in height. In their dense cane thickets only plants species that tolerate shade can establish, and the growth of saplings of various trees is limited although it a question of time before they get their chance to develop. For example the fall down of a huge *Coihue* open a large clearing in the forest. With the entrance of light, plants can grow with great strength.

The more dense cane thickets are formed under the evergreen *Coihue* There the canes find protection from great temperature changes, strong winds, rains or intense snowfall. Also the cover of snow is shorter in time under the *Coihue* than under deciduous trees: the canes may grow again with strength after the snow melts.

In contrast, the density and height of the canes diminishes under the *Lenga*, a deciduous tree. May be because they are less protected from low temperatures and the snow lasts longer. On the other hand, the *Lenga* understory receives much more light during spring than the *Coihue* understory, and various bushes are benefited by this competing with canes. There could also be differences in soils composition under one forest or another.

The *Colihue* canes may reproduce by rhizomes, while the flowering occurs every 17 to 20 years. It has massive flowerings after massive production of seeds. With the abundance of food, the rodent populations (see page 91)

:an get bigger in a short time. With
o many preys present, different
predators will start appearing.

Why do canes produce seeds massively?

The massive synchronised flower-ings of the canes might be the result of strategic evolution. The sudden liberation of thousands of seeds means there is more food than needed for the herbivorous populations that feed on them. In this way, a great number of seeds will survive predators.

The Bushes

I only mention a few representative species, all frequent and generally of wide distribution.

Firebush

The Firebush is one of the most frequent species among bushes in the Patagonian Forests. In the Northern sector (*Neuquén*) it grows like a small tree between seven and eight m in height, while in *Santa Cruz* and *Tierra del Fuego*, it is bush (see page 20).
It develops with preference in open areas with a lot of light, and over sandy and damp soil. It is a pioneer species

(see page 14) where the forest has been cut, that is why it is frequently found on the sides of the roads.
As an adult it is evergreen and its leaves have various shapes. The red flowers are hermaphrodite, arranged in inflorescences that blossom since October. The Green-backed Firecrown acts as its pollinator (see page 77). The fruit is a woody capsule four cm long. It opens in autumn liberating numerous small winged seeds (see page 30).

Chilco or Aljaba

It is a bushy plant that grows between *Neuquén* and *Tierra del Fuego*, mainly close to water courses.

It's beautiful hanging flowers have red sepals up to 2.5 cm long, shape and colour that might show coevolution with hummingbirds (see page 77). The Green-backed Firecrown feeds nectar from different flowers, and in captured individuals, the pollen of the *Chilco* resulted the most abundant. As a first impression, one could think it is the flower that they visit most. However, the conclusion reached was that it is not necessarily like that. The grains of pollen from the *Chilco* have viscous filaments, therefore they adhere more effectively.

To favour the dispersal of seeds, the plant offers a fleshy black fruit, approximately 1cm in diameter.

The Chaura

It is a bush full of branches of up to 1.5 m in height that grows from *Neuquén* to *Tierra del Fuego*. Its leaves can have different shapes and are coriaceous with sharp edges. It gives small white

hanging flowers that bloom in summer The fruit are small berries, from pink to purple in colour, which mature in winter (see page 31).

The Calafate and some relatives:

Michay

They are various bushes of the *Berberis* genus, represented in *Patagonia* by 16 species, distributed from steppe areas to forests.

Its small flowers, from yellow to orange, are joined in clusters and different species of insects pollinate them (see page 70). The fruits are small black-blue berries, with 5 or 6 seeds (see page 29).

The *Michay* is one of the best known in the forest. Its foliage is persistent and the leaves have spiny teeth on their edges. Berberis buxifolia is well known for the taste of their fruit.

The Siete Camisas

It's distribution in *Argentina* goes from *Neuquén* to *Tierra del Fuego* and you

pollinators. The fruit is a black berry with three to four seeds. It is one of the most affected species by the browsing of the Red Deer (see page 105).

• • •

find it close to watercourses. It is a branch bush that reaches two m in height. The leaves are coriaceous with irregularly sharp edges. In spring and summer it gives beautiful hermaphrodite red flowers. The fusion of its sepals form like a tube of up to 1.5 cm. The Green-backed Firecrown is one of its pollinators. Its fruit is a small capsule with a number of seeds.

The Maqui

It is a branch bush that is distributed in the country from *Neuquén* to *Chubut*. It prefers humid places and it is an open air colonising species. It produces small and whitish inflorescences and the insects act as

Plants that grow on other plants: The Epiphytes

The epiphytes are plants that grow on other plants in search of light, without harming their support. In the Valdivian forest, there is a great variety of epiphytes, dominating moss and lichen.

In forests of Alerce on the *Chiloé* Island (*Chile*), five tonnes of epiphytes per hectare have been estimated. In our Valdivian forest the diversity is fewer. Without any doubt, the high precipitation and damp environment favours the plants that grow on other plants. Not having contact with the soil, the atmosphere is their source of water.

Another fact to consider is that there are no tree mammals in the Southern Beech Forests. It has been suggested that these mammals (among which the monkeys dominate) regulate in some way the development of epiphytes, especially on the higher branches they use to get around. This is the case mainly for Neotropical rainforests.

Many species of epiphytes from the Southern Forests are endemic (see page 13) and the relation with the *Nothofagus*, the *Pehuén* and other conifers, could indicate long lasting coevolution.

The layer of lichen, moss and algae may reduce the amount of light that reaches certain green parts of the tree, such as the leaves. Therefore, they can cause harm.

A risk for the epiphytes is the high intensity of ultraviolet radiation (UV-B) that affects the highest parts. However, we know that there are lichens with photo-protective pigments

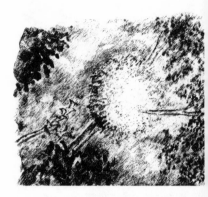

•••

The Hemiparasites

The hemiparasites damage the trees on which they grow by absorbing sap, even though they contain chlorophyll. Their seeds don't develop on the floor. In the Southern Forests there are many species of hemiparasite plants that are endemic. Frequent examples easy to identify are:

The Myzodendron

The *Myzodendron* (Myzodendraceae family) are endemic from the *Nothofagus* forest in *Argentina* and *Chile*. In *Argentina* they appear from *Neuquén* to *Tierra del Fuego*.

They have no leaves and the shapes and colours, yellowish and greenish, of their thin branches make it difficult to miss them among the trees. They give terminal inflorescences and small insects pollinate them. The small mature fruit include long "hairs" (bristle). These help the dispersion by wind and they cling onto other plants to grow on.

The Quintral

It is a hemiparasite plant growing in areas with moderate rainfall, in the Valdivian forest. The leaves are 3 to 6 cm long, and the red flowers, up to 4.5 cm long, are arranged in inflorescences. It flowers between January and May (see page 28) feeding the Green-backed

Firecrown (see page 77) during winter.

Its fruit is a yellowish green berry with one seed and up to 1 cm in diameter. Its very sticky, possibly being an advantage so as to adhere to other plants when dispersed.

•••

Lianas and creepers

The *lianas* are fibrous plants with a very long stem that can go twisting so as to climb over tree trunks in search of light. Many have the help of rings (type of hook) or other methods of griping.

When they reach the crown of a tree, they can hang down and in general, only keep the leaves that receive the most light. The high evaporation in summer may dry them out and the low temperatures in winter freeze the sap.

There are different *lianas* that are endemic species of the forest. It is estimated that 90 % of the creepers in the world are found in the tropics, but in the Valdivian Forest (especially in *Chile*) the diversity is also notorious. The Patagonian Forests have the register of the most austral creepers in the world. In *Los Glaciares* National Park there is only one registered species of *liana*, and there are none known in *Tierra del Fuego*.

The flowers of many lianas and creepers are pollinated by the Green-backed Firecrown. Some of them are:

The Pil-pil Voqui

A *liana* that grows in the dampest areas of the Valdivian Forest: as in *Lago Puelo* National Park; *Puerto Blest* and *Lagunas Frías* (*Nahuel Huapi* National Park).

Its leaves are composite. The red

tubular flowers are 5 cm long and are found on short raceme. They are pollinated by the Green-backed Firecrown. The fruit is in encapsules and up to ten cm long with winged seeds.

The Botellita

It's more frequent from *Neuquén* to *Chubut*. It prefers damp forests. With the help of adventitious roots, it grips on to trees to grow. Its leaves are one to three cm long and have a serrated edge. It flowers from October to February and its beautiful red flowers, up to five cm long, have an important pollinator in the Green-backed Firecrown. It gives green small berries.

The Mutisia

The *Mutisia* is a frequent creeper from *Neuquén* to the south of *Chubut*. Its beautiful flowers (see page 27) are well known and easy to identify.

Another example among the lianas is

the *Pahueldín,* and among the creepers with rings, the *Arvejilla.*

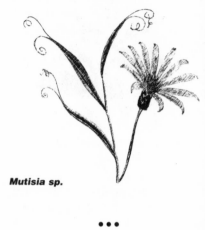

Mutisia sp.

• • •

The Mosses

The mosses may grow on diverse surfaces, as over rocks, on the ground or on fallen or live trunks. They are quite resistant to drying and the wind gives their spores a good capacity of dispersion. But it is in the peat bogs where they represent the dominant vegetation. In *Santa Cruz* and *Tierra del Fuego* there are various peat bogs with *Sphagnum* moss among the most noticeable.

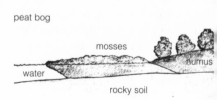

peat bog

mosses

humus

water

rocky soil

The peat bogs are one of the vegetation communities that store more organic carbon per unit of surface in the world. The slow decomposition (due to the cold temperature and scarce oxygen), doesn't allow the carbon captured during the photosynthesis to be liberated.

In the Northern Hemisphere, the peat bogs reach slightly more than 2 m in average depth, and they are known to store up to 108 times more carbon than the Boreal forest. In *Tierra del Fuego* their depths are between 1.5 to 3 m, with extreme cases of 5.5 m. The storage capacity of carbon of South American peat bogs is not known in detail, but it might be high.

Conclusion: burning and draining the peat bogs means the liberation of great volumes of carbon dioxide and they also contain methane. These are two components that in the atmosphere contribute to the greenhouse effect, therefore, global warming.

A specialised flora grows in the peat bogs as is the case of insectivorous plants of the *Drossera* and *Pinguicula* genus.

Drossera

Insectivorous plants

Drossera uniflora is an insectivorous plant found in peat bogs in *Tierra del Fuego* and *Santa Cruz* provinces. In the summer of 1860 Darwin observed leaves of *Drossera* (from an English species) in the process of trapping insects. In search for an explanation, he prepared an experiment: on one side he placed leaves of this plant with a nitrogen fluid. Separately he placed leaves with a fluid lacking nitrogen. Later, only the leaves with the nitrogen fluid were healthy. The naturalist thus got a clue about the benefits of catching insects: they provide nitrogen (from the proteins), a key nutrient that is scarce in the environments where insectivorous plants grow. In the year 1875 Darwin published the book *Insectivorous plants*.

•••

The Lichens

The Southern Beech Forests have a high biomass and diversity of lichens, and the Valdivian Forest, especially in *Chile*, is considered one of the areas of greatest diversity in the world.

The lichens represent one of the most adjusted relations of mutual benefit that is known (symbiosis). An algae and a fungus take part. In most of the cases, the fungus is more developed than the algae, and produces the reproductive structures (fruiting bodies).

The slow growth and the dominance of vegetative reproduction (this means with less sexual reproduction which produces the genetic variation; see page 19), makes the evolution of the lichens slow. For example, there are genus represented both in the Arctic and Antarctic, probably originated in Pangaea (see page 18).

The lichens dominate in environments where they have low competition. They have no capacity to store water so they depend on the rain, fog or dampness in the air. Many can retain nitrogen from the air, therefore they provide nutrients.

As they neither have flowers nor seeds the lichens have practically no relations with insects or birds. They have an effective system of production of chemical defence to avoid being predated.
The lichens known as Old´s man beard (*Usnea* sp.), genus also present in Subantarctic Islands and areas of the Antarctic Peninsula, are abundant and easy to identify in the Patagonian forest.

Old´s man beard (*Usnea sp.*)

● ● ●

The Ferns

The Ferns synthesise lignin, a component of the wood that is the structure of support that allows a tree to reach great size. A step forward in evolution in the plant world compared to the lichens and mosses.
Membranous ferns find a good place to grow on fallen trunks in decomposition.
If the terminal buds of their leaves were to break off, the ferns wouldn't

66

The centres of origin of a group like the fungi that is so antique and diverse must be very different. For example, in the Andean-Patagonian forests there is a cosmopolitan species (*Trametes versicolor*); a species also found in the tropical jungles; and another whose genus (*Descolea*) is found in Australia, New Zealand, New Guinea, India, Siberia and Japan.

The humid forests of *Coihue* and *Guindo* are very favourable for the existence of a variety of fungi. The so called fruiting bodies (reproductive structures that liberate spores) are visible. We see them on the floor, on dead leaves, fallen trunks or parasiting live trees. We can recognise the hat fungi, gelatinous fungi, coraline, and shelf fungi on trunks mainly for their designs.

grow any more. Many obtain more protection by twirling around themselves, for example, against the attack of herbivorous animals.

•••

The Fungus in the Forest

In the *Nothofagus* (see page 51) of the Southern Beech Forests, the mycorrhiza (specific fungi joined to the roots of the tree) plays a key role. On the one hand, they establish connections among the roots, increasing their absorption capacity. But they also offer certain nutrients that help the trees grow in poor lands. For their benefit, the fungi can grow more thanks to substances they get from the *Nothofagus*.

67

The tumours on branches or trunks on our *Nothofagus* are more frequent and well known, and they are produced by the fungi *Cyttaria*, obliged parasite. This is the result of a coevolution that started thousands of years ago.

There are also *Cyttaria* parasiting *Nothofagus* in Australia and New Zealand. Some species of *Cyttaria* are specific, and parasite only one species, while there is one type that parasites five species of *Nothofagus*.

The *Pan de Indio* (*Cyttaria darwinii*) is a weak parasite, and the branch it infects is destined to a slow death, but this doesn't affect the tree. Its fruit-like bodies mature in spring, have a globe-like shape from 2 to 5 cm in diameter and are pale yellow in colour. In *Tierra del Fuego* it was important for the diet of the *Yaghans*, aborigines that lived by the Beagle Channel and other fuegian channels. The *Llao-llao* (*Cyttaria hariotti*) forms "fruits" from 3 to 7 cm that mature between November and January. Larva of flies can infect them. The fungi are consumed by various animals, and the *Cyttaria* are important for the diet of various rodents.

The leaves of the *Roble Pellín* are alternating guests of a fungus that results a pest for the *Pehuén*. As a consequence, these two species can't grow together.

Many fungi produce toxic substances. But this resource can't be explained as a defence against predators surged from natural selection, such as the alkaloids (nicotine, caffeine, etc.), in superior plants.

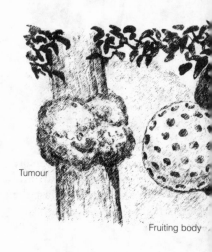

Tumour

Fruiting body

Cyttaria sp.

Fauna

The insects

Different groups of insects (and spiders) from our Southern Beech Forests forests have similarities with those in New Zealand, Tasmania and Australia (see page 18).

The organic soil layers, plants and animals in decomposition and the fungi keep on a diverse and abundant fauna of insects. On trees and bushes the amount and diversity of insects tends to be smaller, and it diminishes from north to south.

Insects and flowers

Four groups are the main actors among pollinating insects in the forests (see page 14). Because of the unstable climate, the pollinators must have been pressed in their evolution to have a wide spectrum of food supply. It is too risky to bet everything to one option.

In general, the Coleoptera (among which we find the beetles) aren't specialised in pollinating, and usually visit big flowers.
The Diptera (flies) are better adapted. They have more or less developed pricks to suck nectar. Although their diet is varied, it includes excrement also. The Lepidoptera (butterflies and moths) are more specialised for pollination.

But the Hymenoptera (bees) are the most efficient pollinators. They need to collect nectar for their hive too, and in consequence must visit hundreds of flowers every day to satisfy their needs. They have developed complex systems of communicating. With special dances, the workers communicate to their peers the distance, location and richness of the source of food. The sun is the reference to guide them. The most attractive forms may be found in the bumble bee (*Bombus sp*) frequently observed.

A research in the *Puyehue* National Park (*Chile*) has brought up interesting results. After 1049 periods of observation that lasted 10 minutes each (between October and November 1987 and January and February 1988), 51 species of pollinating insects were counted. The greater or less activity depended mainly on the temperature. The group of the bees was the most active, followed by flies, butterflies and Coleoptera.
Some butterflies perforate the corolla of flowers to take their nectar, therefore not acting as pollinators in

Bumble bee

these cases (as they don't come in contact with the pollen).

The plants visited by many insects (like the *Michay*, see page 60) were dominants, although some had a specific pollinator.

The flowers also may result a good refuge or place for mating for the insects. In the morning you can find insects protected in the interior of flowers that close in the dark.

In spring till mid summer, you can look for insects co-operating with flowers. A magnifying glass will help you observe many details. Towards the south, the diversity of insects diminishes.

Insects affecting plants .

At least 120 species of insects feed or harm in some way the *Nothofagus* in *Argentina* and *Chile*. The conifers, with their resin, are more resistant.

There are groups that attack the leaves, like the caterpillars of the Geometridae butterflies. The bagworm is famous defoliating larvae of the *Lenga* (Saturniidae family)
In *Nothofagus* in general, the foliage becomes less palatable as years go by, diminishing the risk of attack from herbivorous insects. In 1986, the leaves of more than 100,000 hectares of *Lenga* forests in *Nahuel Huapi* National Park and *Lanín* National Park were severely damaged.

Other insects perforate the bark and damage the wood. Also, the openings they produce may be the entrance for fungi. The oldest and hardest vegetable tissue usually accumulates tannin, of defensive function. In *Neuquén* there are records off damage by the Cerambicidae beetles. The woodpeckers (see page 75) help to control this.

The tannin

The basic element to synthesise tannin is sugar, and it is elaborated by photosynthesis (it doesn't require nitrogen, a component that can be a limiting factor). The tannin makes the digestion difficult and cause the coagulation of proteins to the herbivorous animals that ingest it.

The sap sucking insects in our *Nothofagus* forest present a close relation with groups that affect the *Nothofagus* in other continents. Various insects consume seeds, like the Lepidoptera of the *Perzelia* genus.

The galls are a defensive answer to the attack of certain insects (also against fungi, bacteria and algae). They offer refuge and also concentrate nutrients, resulting in a good place for larvas of acharid insects. The intruders even stop depending on green parts of the plant (of seasonal production, in the forest). That is why the galls are abundant in temperate climates.

But, what benefit does the plant obtain by producing galls?
It has been suggested that by offering home and food, the plants are able to restrict their invaders there, without affecting their condition. It is frequent to find galls in the leaves of the *Lenga*.

•••

The Amphibians

The amphibians in the Southern Beech Forests belong to an antique group with many endemisms (see page 13), but there is also a group with affinities with an Australian group of amphipians.
The diversity is not high, it decreases

towards the south and the group is absent in *Tierra del Fuego*.

The low temperatures affect various aspects of their life; however they reach a certain seasonal adaptation. The cold retards the development of its eggs and larvas, and inhibits its metamorphosis.
In areas where the *Pehuén* grows you can find the *Sapo Andino*. On clear days it was proved that its temperature rises to 32 °C, this means 15 °C over its external temperature in the shade. The temperature can't go any higher because it regulates it by evaporation.

The *Sapo del Bosque* from the *Nothofagus* forests, is known for laying eggs in cold waters at temperatures between 1 and 7° C.

The amphibians usually stay in a determined area to eat, reproduce and have young. They may even recognise the design of the coast, guiding their movements in reference to it. The knowledge of the terrain allows its survival: it's good to know where to take refuge, where to find food and where to find competitors and predators.

There are species which mimic the colours of the vegetation and little adhesive disks on their fingers helps them to climb.
Some species were discovered in recent decades and their distribution is very restricted. The *Rana de*

Chalhuaco is a relict species, strictly endemic of the *Nahuel Huapi* National Park, and the *Ranita Andina* is exclusive in *Argentina* in the Valdivian Forest and the *Nahuel Huapi* National Park.

To avoid predators is a necessity. Eggs and larva of frogs may be unpalatable. The toxic substances in glands of the skin apparently would also be deposited on the eggs. But the tadpoles are without any doubt a good prey. Many amphibians have reproductive cycles that may have evolved as a strategy to diminish the risk of predation, or environmental changes. The toads are the group of terrestrial vertebrates with the greatest number of reproductive systems.

In the Valdivian Forest, both in *Argentina* and *Chile*, you find a fantastic example of specialization: the tiny Darwin's Frog. It lives in damp areas, close to shallow streams and it would be associated among others to the Nalca.

You have to be an expert to find them, but to know that such a peculiar organism exists, increases our admiration for Nature. Let's see its life's cycle:
The males and females liberate their respective gametes together. After the external fecundation, the eggs develop in damp soils approximately for 20 days. The males stay around and when muscular activity is detected in the embryos in formation, takes the

Darwin's frog

advanced eggs into his roomy vocal pouch. They keep them there, and after three days the larvas hatch. A viscous fluid that surrounds them will provide nutrition. After about 50 days, between 5 and 15 little froglets emerge through

The Australian example

The Darwin's Frog is known since the XIX century. In 1973, an even more specialized case (see page 14) was discovered: the australian *Rheobatrachus*. The female kept the young in her stomach. It was proved that the eggs liberated prostaglandins in charge of suppressing the acid secretions of the stomach. The mothers didn't eat during all the development. No individuals of this species have been found since 1981. It must be extinct.

their father's mouth. All along this process, the male can eat to nurture.

— • —

The Reptiles

The reptiles of the forest have little diversity. They are small in size and are dominated by various species of lizards of the *Liolaemus* genus. Among the Ophids, the endemic *Culebra Valdiviana* is the only species that is registered in the Southern Forest.
The possibility of observing lizards is

Liolaemus sp.

greater in the summer months. They are seen mostly on the coasts of lakes. Also, over timberline or close to the steppe. There they find different arthropods to eat, the possibility to

warm up in the rays of the sun, and a good refuge in the rocks. Also in areas of the Pehuén forest or near dry trunks of the *Nothofagus* forest.

In species of colder climates, storing reserves is a need and the base of the tail is a good place for it. In the case of autotomy, common in lizards, the cut occurs towards the end like that the stored fats aren't lost.

It has been suggested that during the glaciations, the lizards concentrated in low lands. When the ice melted, they colonised diverse habitats in elevated areas, being isolated one from the other. A good condition for the origin of new endemic species.

The *Culebra Valdiviana* is poisonous but not mortal. Is restricted to forest environments between *Neuquén* and north-west *Chubut*. The Darwin's frog, among other amphibians, is their many food suppy.

— • —

The Birds

Fewer than fifty species of birds live in the Southern Beech Forests of *Argentina* and *Chile* only considering the birds that nest, eat and live in the forest or its boundaries. The Valdivian forest holds almost twenty species, while in the less diverse Andean Cypress forest you can find eleven to thirteen species.

Numbers increase if you take in account the species that enter the forest temporarily.

Different to groups of plants, insects, spiders and some amphibians, the birds of this region don't have any relation with the ancient continent of Gondwana (see page 18).

On the other hand, in spite of the isolation of the forests, the birds capacity to fly has enabled them a good exchange and dispersion from and with neighbouring environments. Many (excluding the aquatic birds) are related with the birds of the Patagonian steppe. There is also relation with the birds of the *Puna*

and even the birds of the Andean forests in South and North America.

Several birds of the forest are distributed from *Neuquén* to *Tierra del Fuego*. Their tolerance to the changing environmental conditions would be the result of natural selection during the glacial periods. They can also occupy diverse habitats, a characteristic proper of birds in isolated environments. Some species require specific habitats.

Small populations of birds that live on patches of forest have more risk of decreasing in number in difficult years or because of some illness, for example. The genetic variation is reduced in small and isolated populations (see page 19).

Exclusiveness and years

Approximate percentages of endemic bird species (see page 13) of different forests, according to their time of isolation (see page 5).

Place	% of endemic birds	years of isolation
Tasmania	20 %	12,000 years
Southern Forests	41 %	10 million years
New Zealand	80 %	50 million years

Note: Tasmania had its last connection with Australia during the glaciations (when the sea levels went down), but before this, there were thousands of years of isolation.

It is considered that various species don't have enough territory in small patches in the Valdivian forest. This is the case of the Chilean Pigeon, the Magellan Woodpecker, the Black-throated Huet-huet, the Austral Parakeet, and hawks.

Next I mention some representative birds of the forest according to their main food source (but not exclusively), distributed from *Neuquén* to *Tierra del Fuego* (except where I say otherwise).

Birds that feed on insects:

The woodpeckers

male

male

Magellan Woodpecker

The Magellan Woodpecker, the Chilean Flicker and the Striped Woodpecker are the three species of the Picidae family in the Southern Beech Forests.

The Magellan Woodpecker, the largest in South America, lives mainly in mature, little disturbed Southern Beech Forest, and also mixed Andean Cypress forest.
It forms couples or family groups. It finds food, like eggs, larvas or adult insects, both in trunks or on branches of trees.
As most woodpeckers, this species drum trunks with its strong and sharp bill to establish and maintain its territory and to find partner. They also have various voices. Special adaptations protect the brain from all the drumming.
The Magellan Woodpecker chooses partially dead trees to make their nest (see page 33). In the fuegian forest the most frequent holes for the nests were between five and fifteen meters in height, with cavities of various forms and oriented in every direction. The reproductive season starts in November.

The Chilean Flicker, on the other hand, is usually found in the ecotone or clearings in the forest and its observation may be easier. They move in couples or family groups. They look for food both in vegetation as well as in fallen tree trunks on the ground. Hollows in trees and in caves on slopes are adequate nesting places.

The Thorn-tailed Rayadito

It is one of the most abundant species of birds in the forest from *Neuquén* to *Tierra del Fuego*. They move swiftly on trunks and short branches, with short flights and low height. With the help of their beak they trap various insects in constant search; under the bark, or in crevices and hollows of the tree, or among moss and lichen. On Staten Island some have been observed searching in kelps (*Macrocystis pyrifera*) on the coast. They also feed on small fruit.

They are found mainly in transition areas between the steppe and the forest, or in the interior of the *Nothofagus* forests, and in bushy areas. They tend to form small bands, more frequently with the Patagonian *Sierra-Finch*, the Rufous-collared Sparrow and the White-throated Treerunner (a species that resembles woodpecker's behaviour, climbing up trees).

They nest in hollows in trees and between November and December they lay three to four eggs.

Their noisy singing gives away their presence and this is a curious example of how they bothered the Shelknams (*Onas*) when they hunted *guanacos*.

The Chucao Tapaculo and the Black-throated Huet-huet

Both are inhabitants of the Valdivian Forest, between *Neuquén* and *Chubut* in *Argentina*. They belong to a family practically exclusive of the Southern Forests, the Rhinocriptidae.

They have fairly long and strong legs, adapted to living on the ground. They are good walkers, often raising their tail and mimicking colour to protect themselves. They live in couples and result in being heard more than seen.

Its varied diet changes in relation to what the forest offers, according to the seasons, but they mainly eat insects. In the stomach contents of a

Chucao Tapaculo

insect group related to the myrtle family, the one of the major diversity in the forest (the *Arrayán* being the best known).

• • •

Birds that feed on flower's nectar:

The Green-backed Firecrown

Chucao Tapaculo (in *Chiloe*), invertebrates –with mites of the *Curculionidae* family among the most representative–, and seeds were found. It has been suggested that the high frequency of these mites may depend on their abundance, being an

The Green-backed Firecrown is unique in the forest among birds that base their diet in the nectar of flowers. As pollinator, it is considered a key species (see page 14).

It is distributed from *Neuquén* to *Tierra del Fuego*, and occasionally it has been registered in the *Malvinas* (Falklands) Islands. In winter it moves sometimes to the south of *Buenos Aires*, *La Pampa* and *Córdoba*.

On cold days it seeks refuge in hollows in trees or in rocks, where it remains dormant. It makes its nest with lichens, mosses and plant fibres.

In spite of being practically the only hummingbird in this environment, up to fourteen species of plants with tubular red flowers grow in the forest (there are less in the austral area). You will find shapes and colours that usually indicate a close relation with this bird (see page 28). There are

Black-throated Huet-huet

77

(*Arrayanes* forest) were the places under study.

In *Puerto Blest* the hummingbird was seen as from the end of September, being more abundant during the reproductive stage between November and December, lowering in number towards the end of summer and beginning of autumn, and not detected in winter. In the *Quetrihué* Peninsula, it was detected all year round probably because of the *Quintral* flowering in winter.

This hummingbird is an efficient pollinator: of over fifty individuals captured, forty eight carried pollen of more than one plant species (this indicates that they may visit many species in a short time).

Among the most visited flowers there was a predominance of the red coloured, tubular in shape and with corollas varying from one to six centimeters in length. Such is the case of the flowers in many bushes (*Siete Camisas*; Firebush; *Fuchsia*; *Botellita, Taique*), creepers like the *Pil-pil Voqui* (see page 63), and the *Quintral*.

The volume of nectar per flower varied, but the concentrations of sugars resulted much more constant. They seldom exceed 25% of the concentration, but in the flowers in the forest visited they almost all exceeded it.

other birds species that include nectar as part of their generalist diet, condition associated to the geographical isolation (see page 5). But it is not clear if these birds act as pollinators or not.

The majority of the plants pollinated by the Green-backed Firecrown, flower in spring and summer (dry season) and in step sequences. The *Quintral* (see page 62) is an important exception, flowering in autumn and winter, and it doesn't grow in *Santa Cruz* and *Tierra del Fuego*. The hummer populations in those latitudes, that are in fact scarce, must migrate to the north before the cold months.

In a recent study in the area of *Nahuel Huapi* National Park, valuable information was obtained. *Puerto Blest* and the Peninsula de *Quetrihué*

The hummingbirds are endemic from America, but there are groups of unrelated birds that have a comparable ecological role: the Meliphagouss. They are found in Africa, areas in Australia and New Guinea. They also pollinate flowers rich in nectar, and the species of longer beaks relate more with flowers of long corollas, red or orange in colour. But differently to the hummingbird, they don't feed while flying. Their strong legs with short fingers and long nails help them survive in tough places, allowing a good access to the flowers.

Flowers and sugar

Many flowers pollinated by hummingbirds offer between 20 % and 25% of sugar in nectar. Although in the laboratory it was proved that certain hummingbirds prefer (if offered) a more energetic nectar, with concentrations up to 45%.

Why aren't there any flowers usually pollinated by hummingbirds with such high concentrations of sugar?

With higher concentrations, the viscosity of the nectar increase. In consequence, the volume that can get to the tongue through capillarity is smaller. The maximum efficiency of suction for small volumes of nectar was determined for concentrations of 20 to 25 %.

Also the resources invested in nectar by the plant must be taken into account. The concentrations may change notoriously according to the environmental conditions, in particular the changes in humidity. In comparison, bees take fewer volumes of nectar but more concentrated.

• • •

Birds that base their diet on fruit and seeds:

A high percentage of the plants in the forest, mainly in the Valdivian area, offer fleshy fruit. However, few bird species base their diet on those fruit.

The fact is that there are birds with a more generalist diet that also contribute to seed dispersion. Just like Sierra-finches, Chucao Tapaculo, Black-throated Huet-huet and even the Chimango Caracara, as well as mammals.

Considering birds that eat fruit as an additional resource, the number of species is close to twenty. Most of them also feed on insects or are carnivores.

Before winter, up to 50 % of the bird

species of the Southern Forests migrate to the north, or close to forests that are at a lower height over sea level. In some cases, only part of the population moves. Luckily (or better said, by coevolution between plants and animals), they have many mature fruit to get reserves of energy before they leave (see page 31). In the temperate forests in North-America, winters are harsher and more than 75 % of the birds migrate.

The reasons for migrations would be the unfavourable climate and the decrease of food. Bird groups depend on seasonal foods, such as flowers and fruits. They have a higher proportion of migrating species compared to the carnivorous, insectivorous or varied diet birds.

The Austral Parakeet

It is found from *Neuquén* to *Tierra del Fuego* and it is the southernmost parrot in the world. The southern populations are larger than the ones in the north (see page 96).

They are found mainly in the forests of *Pehuén*, *Nothofagus*, and Winter's bark, and sometimes in open spaces. They move over tree tops looking for seeds. The Austral Parakeet also eat seeds of *Chusquea* canes, berries from bushes or seeds on the ground and tender shoots of the *Nothofagus*. As all parrots, they predate seeds but they also act as dispersers (see page 29).

They form couples or small groups, even though their movements may be more numerous. As from autumn, especially towards the southern region, they descend the mountain sides looking for forests free of snow and more protected.

They establish their nests in hollows of trees or in dense cane fields, with the help of plant material. The female incubates and feeds the baby during the first stages of life, while the male provides the food through regurgitation.

In the Valdivian forest in *Chile*, lives a close relative, the *Choroy* (see page 49).

Birds of varied diet:

The White-crested Elaenia: small and restless

It belongs to the *Elaenia genus* (Tyrannidae family; considered mostly as of insectivorous diet), being this species one of the most abundant in the forest during spring and summer from *Neuquén* to *Tierra del Fuego*. Although mainly insectivorous, it has a varied diet. It has been considered a key species (see page 14) as a seed disperser. It may even act as pollinator in some cases, but this is not certain. For example, it visits the flowers of the Firebush. This bird is very active. In summer, it prefers the small fleshy fruit from the bushes. It is known that they eat fruit from the *Maitén, Arrayán, Michay, Calafate*, possibly the *Quintral* and the *Parrilla*. In areas of peat bogs there are bushes that give fruit in winter (see page 31) and the White-crested Elaenia can also take advantage of them.

Its different songs help to detect this species. It moves alone or in couples and forms small groups when migrating.

The Austral Thrush

It is found from *Neuquén* to *Tierra del Fuego*. Occupies various habitats in argentine forests, but it is more abundant in ecotone areas. It even increases in numbers in forested islands that result from deforestation (a major problem in *Chile*). It has been considered that in these places they compensate the decrease of other birds in the dissemination of seeds. The Austral Thrush is one of the most common species in parks and gardens.

It's found alone or in couples and its melodious song identifies it. Its diet is varied, finding various arthropods and snails, and even fruit on the ground. The nest is a bowl of plant fibres that it constructs on trees; they lay eggs twice or three times a year.

The Chilean Pigeon

The Chilean Pigeon is one of the largest among the wild species of its family in *Argentina*. It has been associated a lot to the forests of *Maitén*, *Arrayán*, Andean Cypress and *Coihue*. Scarce in *Santa Cruz* province, occasionally gets to *Tierra del Fuego*. It may be a seed disperser.

It forms couples and between spring and summer it nests. It constructs a platform with sticks on branches of trees or on *Chusquea* canes. It lays one egg and occasionally two. Flocks of up to one hundred chilean pigeons can be formed in autumn and winter.

A characteristic of the family in general, is the production of milk to feed its chicks (similar composition to mammalian milk). It is an adaptation that ensures a source predictable and rich in nutrients in the critical stages of the chicks. The population of the Chilean Pigeon is recovering from a virus that caused great mortality in the decade of 1950.

• • •

Scavengers and birds of prey in or near the Forest:

The Andean Condor

The King of the *Andes* has a wide distribution in South America, nesting all along the *Andes*.
You can observe it in all the area of distribution of the Southern Beech Forests. Its magnificent soaring flight may have evolved in the need to save energy during their long air voyages looking for carrion, its main source of food. But it doesn't have the swiftness and speed to manoeuvre of its ancestors, predators.
Being carcasses a scarce resource, when available the *Condor* can eat

and store food. Flying with a full stomach complicates matters, but it can regurgitate when in danger.

The naked skin on its head and neck are adaptations to prevent the feathers getting dirty when they stick their head into a dead animal. On the other hand they are well adapted to tolerate the bacterial toxins in rotten meat.

The good insulation of their feathers protects them from the very low temperatures as those registered in the heights of flight. The crest and ruggedness of the skin represent a great exposed surface to gain or lose heat quickly.

They nest in solitary couples and the only egg laid is incubated fifty five days. The parents feed the chick by regurgitation. Its defence of the nest is not the best and predation is the most important reason for its loss.

The extensive period of paternal care determines that it must nest as a maximum every one year and a half. After six years they are mature to reproduce.

A successful conservation project of the Andean Condor was developed in the *Buenos Aires* Zoological Garden, including artificial incubation techniques.

male

female

Andean Condor

The Andean Condor has one chick every two or three years in its natural environment. In captivity, when the first egg is taken away, they lay a second one. The eggs are incubated and when the chicks are born, they are raised in isolation. With skilful puppets that represent their parents, the direct contact with humans is avoided. Juvenile have been liberated in some regions in *Argentina* and in other South American countries.

In *Patagonia*, the first place chosen to liberate them is the area of *Valle Encantado, Neuquén*. It was proved that they have integrated with the wild condors, and the project continues monitoring the evolution of these individuals with modern solar satellite transmitters.

The Black-chested Buzzard Eagle

The Black-chested Buzzard

been observed over all the

About size

Among the largest flying birds in the world, apart from the Andean Condor, there are representatives of the families of the pelicans, geese, eagles and albatross. Which is the largest of them all? Not so easy to say, but it is interesting the fact that they are all in a similar range: from 13 to 15 kg in weight and between 3 and 3,5 m in wingspan. Physical limitations, as the energy that the flight muscles can generate, wouldn't allow more weight or bigger dimensions.

Although fossil records discovered in *Argentina* show that the Argentavis magnificens with a wingspan of 7 m, would be the largest flying bird known of up to now that ever existed on the world.

The size and sex

The female of the Black-chested Buzzard Eagle is larger than the male. The difference in size between sexes is frequent in many species of diurnal birds of prey. In extreme cases, the female is one and a half larger than the male.

What force of natural selection determined these variations in size according to the sex?

Let's start commenting certain observations. The vultures and the Condor are scavengers, and don't have great difference in size between sexes. The Crested Caracara and the Chimango Caracara, of varied diet including prey, don't either. The Snail Kite, that eats snails, has very small differences. In species that eat insects and reptiles it is a bit more notorious. While in rapacious that eat birds while flying, the difference is very noticeable. The Bicoloured Hawk, inhabitant of the forest, is specialised in hunting birds.

It seems that among rapacious birds that hunts agile or dangerous prey, the difference in size is greater. The generalisations always leave some out, but a conclusion would be that the males seem to be more agile and efficient hunters the smaller they are. They are among the ones favoured by natural selection.

On the other hand, the topic may be related to reproduction. The females compete for territories where to nest. It is an advantage to be greater in size. Therefore natural selection favours the bigger females. The Black-chested Buzzard Eagle is in an intermediate situation, balanced between hunting and reproduction. In proportion, the major difference in size between sexes in this species is given in the wing span of the females.

reas in the beech forest. With its ong and wide wings, it's a good glide nd makes efficient use of warm air urrents.

This eagle prefers open vegetation reas to hunt. Its wide diet includes birds, small rodents, reptiles, the European hare and even carrion. It varies a lot according to the area, a sign of its plasticity and opportunism.

It is a solitary eagle and forms a couple for its lifetime. Their voices are important during courtship, in their aggressive conduct and also in relation to the food.

It nests on big trees or cliff edges, and one to three eggs are laid at intervals from three to five days. After one month of incubation, the eggs hatch and the chicks have a great competition between themselves.

The Crested Caracara and the White-throated Caracara

The Crested Caracara has a wide distribution in *Argentina* and inhabits a variety of environments. It can be found in all the forest areas.

They move alone or in small groups and sometimes they are seen next to vultures while they feed, trying to obtain a mouthful of some dead animal. Their long legs allow them to move quickly and safely on the ground, and the wide wings an acceptable soaring. They are usually seen on branches, on the ground and also flying.

In their varied diet they include carrion and they even steal food from other animals, usually rapacious birds and gulls.

They nest in solitary couples, laying three to four eggs at a time. They hatch in a quite synchronised manner as they aren't incubated till there are two or three eggs. The female looks after and feed the chicks while the male looks for food.

The White-throated Caracara belong to the same genus (*Polyborus*) a the Crested Caracara. It inhabit exclusively the areas of the Southern forests, though scarce and of les frequent observation.

White-throated Caracara

The Austral Pigmy Owl

This owl can be found from *Neuquén* to *Tierra del Fuego*, migrating in winter to areas in the centre o *Argentina*. It is an inhabitant in the forest, many times close to clearing or in areas with dead trees (see page 33). This species establishes it nests in tree hollows. It's quite active during daytime, even though its feeding habits aren't well known Birds and small rodents are it main preys.

Near *Bahia Lapataia* (*Tierra del Fuego* National Park) a strange behaviour was detected. The owl being observed regurgitated and flew to a nearby bush and from there he took a hairy mouse The Austral Pigmy Owl had it hidden there, and with its prey in its feet i

the area of the forests, between *Neuquén* and *Tierra del Fuego*, always in low density. It bases its diet on fish, and its elongated neck and large bill are adaptations to capture food.

Their large legs situated far back and their lobed toes make them good swimmers. Grebes in general are well

lew to a cliff to try to hide it again. ts behaviour may be an adaptation o life in cold regions. On the one nand, the captured prey doesn't lecompose quickly. On the other nand, low temperatures diminish animal activity and also preys (as rodents) may have sudden population changes, from abundance to scarcity. In this uncertain scenario, stocking reserves must be a convenient strategy for the Austral Pigmy Owl.

• • •

Waterfowl

The Great Grebe and some relatives

The Great Grebe is frequently seen in rivers, streams, lakes and lagoons in

---

Menu with special ingredients: feathers

The grebes are unique in the habit of eating their own feathers, even more among the fish eaters. In some species, they even have been observed feeding feathers to their just born chicks.

In what way are they benefited? The feathers decompose and mix with food in the main chamber of the stomach. Every now and then they regurgitate the feathers in pellets with non digestible parts of fish. The pellets of feathers protect the stomach and retard the digestion in such a way that sharp and dangerous bones reach the intestines almost dissolved. Another advantage is to eliminate the risk of getting parasites from the fish. Actually, grebes have fewer parasites than other birds whose diets are based on fish.

Great Grebe

eggs. Nests float reducing the risk of terrestrial predators like mammals being birds their main predators. Such is the case of the Kelp Gull which population has expanded from the coast towards the *Andes* partly because of food supply increase related to human activities.

Other species of grebes frequently seen in the lakes and lagoons in areas near the forests are the White-tufted Grebe and the Silvery Grebe.

adapted to diving, and its skeleton has less buoyancy than other birds. Their brief diving with its wings folded is no deeper than seven metres, but in general it only does superficial immersions. Its dense feathers are waterproof, and the skin a good protection from the humidity.

They are rarely seen on land or in flight. When they shed their feathers, they lose the capacity to fly for three to four weeks till they replace them. The vocalisations differentiate the species, but also the sexes and even give proper identity. The voice of the *Huala* in the patagonian lakes is a well known sound.

The couples are usually together during the breeding season that is fairly long, including elaborate courtship rituals between both sexes. In the Great Grebe, the ritual is more vocalised.

They breed over platforms in shallow waters and lay between two and seven

The Torrent Duck

The Torrent Duck includes a sub species distributed from *Neuquén* to *Tierra del Fuego*. This duck lives in couples or small family groups. Male and female looks quiet different being the male the most noticeable with its colourful plumage.

It inhabits rough water courses where you can see it on rocks or trunks near the water. These environments usually have a high concentration of oxygen, a good supply and recirculation of nutrients, and a rapid decomposition of organic material. These conditions favour the biological diversity, with an abundance of insect larvas, molluscs, and even small fish.

As an adaptation to the environment the Torrent Duck, in addition to the webbed toes, has a long and strong

ail. Also, a layer of air between its
eathers allows a good protection
rom the low temperatures and it
ncreases its buoyancy. It flies
ittle and not very high. Its
pecialisation represents a long
unning coevolution with habitat
hat nowadays are more disturbed
nd modified by man activity.

Jnlike other ducks that nest in rivers,
he Torrent Duck is not very sociable.
The couple maintain a territory
luring all year round by the male
ong range sound audible over the
ough waters. This species nests in
rooves or cavities between roots of
rees. Laying up to five eggs, the

female has a long incubation period
of about forty four days, while the
male stays nearby.

– • –

The Mammals

The diversity of mammals in the
Southern Beech Forests is low in
relation to the temperate forests
of North America. On the other
hand, there are no large native
mammals that may be compared to
bears or elks.

In relation to the closer subtropical
forests (in the North West of
Argentina) and considering mid-size
to small mammals, in the Southern
Forests there are neither monkeys
nor squirrels, and the diversity of bats
is low. Taking into account the
small species, in the Southern
Forests there are many endemic
species (see page 13).

The climatic and geological
changes of the past may be
responsible for the present
low diversity in these
forests. During the
glaciations, for example,
the scarce capacity of
dispersion of the mammals
may have limited their
possibilities to adapt. The
majority of them aren't good long

Male

Female

distances travellers to spread from or to isolated environments. They don't resist much time without food and even less without water. Also the adult mammal needs a couple, and young needs a mother.

In the Patagonian forests the diversity and density of mammals in general decreases southwards, while towards the west crossing to *Chile*, there are less variations.

Who is who among the mammals of the forest?

The Monito de Monte

It is an endemic and scarce marsupial from the Valdivian Forest and the only living representative of the Microbiotheridae family. It's distrib-uted in *Argentina* from *Lanín* to *Los Alerces* National Park. Together with a species of rodent, it is the only arboreal mammal in the region.

It is ten to twelve cm long resembling a small rodent. Its prehensile and long hairy tail and its feet are adapted to climbing trees. The big eyes are an adaptation to its nocturnal habits.

The invertebrates, among them insects and larvas, dominate their varied diet. They form couples at least during the breeding season. The female gives birth three to five youngs

and when they are born they climb to the marsupial (bag with four nipple in this species) until the female keep them in nests on trunks or between canes. After this stage, the mother may transport them and even after they become independent, they are still very close to their mother.

With the arrival of the cold season the Monito de Monte hibernate decreasing its heart beating and using up the fat stored in its tail.

Monito de Monte

A different strategy: being a marsupial

The kangaroos (native of Australia) represent the most famous group of marsupials. Their offspring develop in their bags or marsupials. In *Argentina* the opossums are the best known.

What basic difference is there between the marsupials and the placental mammals, as our human species, that give birth to a young completely developed?

The answer would be the effort invests during the different stages of growth. In the marsupials, the young are born in an almost embryo stage and totally defenceless. Its main nutrition comes from the lactation period.

In the placental, on the other hand, the main nutrition comes from the placenta, a protected environment. The babies are born with a degree of development and its lactation stage in general is rather short.

The marsupials may have an advantage in unpredictable and changing climatic conditions. The young will probably die but the parents will survive, and very soon start the reproduction in better conditions. In the placental mammals the bad times may mean the death of both the baby and the mother. But in the balance of advantages and disadvantages under the pressure of natural selection, the strategy of the placental is more successful.

The rodents

The rodents are a very diverse group among the mammals in the Andean-Patagonian forest. They usually find refuge in fallen trunks and dense cane fields, a good place to keep away from the rapacious birds. Close to the steppe many are predated by owls.

A study of the mammals in the region of *Torres del Paine* National Park (*Chile*) produced interesting results.

The area covers less than 1 % of the country surface, but it includes more than 50 % of the mammal species in *Chile*. There are two determining factors: the high habitat diversity and the possibility of species to migrate from neighbouring areas.

This region has been connected to neighbour environments. The fauna in central *Chile*, however, remained isolated since the glaciations (the *Andes* are a great barrier). Therefore the mammals in *Torres del Paine* come

91

from different sources: the Valdivian forest, the Austral or Magellan forest, the Andean region and the Patagonian steppe.

Similar evidence was found between the forest and the steppe close to lake *Nahuel Huapi*. The diversity and density of mammals that are less than 200 grams was twice as much than in neighbouring forest areas. Sixteen species of small rodents were caught, a number of diversity much greater than any other forest or tropical jungle.

However, food doesn't seem to be enough for them. The *Nothofagus* don't produce fleshy nuts as there are in the forests in the Northern Hemisphere. Also these mammals have less alternate strategies than those in the north, such as hibernating during the cold months.

Their main sources of food would be the seeds from the canes, numerous larva of big beetles and the abundant fungi. Among the rodents in the forest, diverse *Tuco-tuco* stand out, as well as the southern race of Coypu, inhabitants of streams and rivers between *Neuquén* and *Tierra del Fuego*.

Wolves, felines and rapacious birds are important in the control of population of rodents and other small mammals.

A very special rodent: the Social Tuco-tuco

The species of *Tuco-tuco* are adapted to underground life. Among them the Social Tuco-tuco is strictly endemic

Social Tuco-tuco

in the *Nahuel Huapi* and though it isn't an inhabitant in the forest, it is worth mentioning it. Its presence is known in the western valley of the *Limay* river and the *mallines* (wet lands) are its dominant habitat. Its incisive teeth, long nails and short muscular legs are adaptations to dig. Its eyes are small and its sense of smell and hearing are well developed, as it lives in a dark environment.

They form numerous colonies, and their sociability is a noticeable feature that distinguishes them from the other *Tuco-tuco*. They have a litter of six per year.

In a recent study, it was proved that some of the colonies were disappearing. Cattle raising and pines plantation were affecting them. On the other hand, some colonies were mortal victims of an illness (*Tuleramia*) caused by bacteria carried by the European Hare (an exotic species, see page 101). As they form colonies, the transmission could cause havoc. Also, a potential dam on the *Limay* river would flood part of their habitat.

Another rodent of restricted distribution is the *Tunduco*, of dominant underground life. They have only been detected in areas of *Lanín* National Park and north of *Nahuel Huapi* National Park.

The Bats

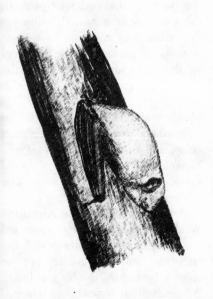

The abundance and diversity of bats is scarce in the Southern Forests. The fact is that in almost all the temperate forests in the world there is a shortage of bats.

In *Argentina* there are from three to five known species of this winged group dominating the insectivorous. They form small colonies from thirty to forty members that seek refuge under the bark, in hollow trunks or in small caves.

The *Murcielago colorado* with reddish brown hair is the most representative. It leads a solitary life, feeds on nocturnal insects like butterflies and beetles. It has a litter of two and it can hibernate in winter.

The Deers

The Huemul

The *Huemul* is an endemic species from the Andean-Patagonian forests. Distributed in restricted areas from *Argentina* and *Chile*, is an endangered species. In *Argentina* isolated populations can be found between *Neuquén* and *Santa Cruz*. It was declared National Natural Monument and Provincial Natural Monument in *Santa Cruz*, *Chubut* and *Río Negro* provinces.

It is robust with thick dense hair and short legs, adaptations to the environment. The males have forked

Huemul

Female

Male

eat in open areas and then entering the forest for refuge.

They are on heat in autumn and at the beginning of winter the males lose their antlers. After six or seven months of gestation, at the end of spring and beginning of summer, the females give birth. The Red Fox and the Black-chested Buzzard Eagle may predate them, while the *Puma* may even attack the adult *Huemul*.

The isolation of the populations, the destruction of their environment, the fires, the hunting, the competition with the cattle rearing and the illnesses that these may transmit, as well as introduced species like the Red Deer are different causes that have left the *Huemul* in a critical situation.

antlers, and are bigger than the females. They move alone or in groups of two or three members: a male and his female and young or just females. In winter they may form larger groups. During summer they inhabit steep lands or even elevations over timberline. With the arrival of the cold months, they descend to the forests looking for sunny slopes and protected valleys.

Its herbivorous diet varies from winter to summer according to the habitat. It includes stems, leaves and flowers of herbs, and bushes like the *Notro*, *Maqui*, *Chilco* and *Chaura*. In the forest it browses new shoots of *Lenga* and also *Roble Pellín*, in the northern sector. It seems to prefer to

Many populations are small and isolated and are found in the *Nahuel Huapi*, *Los Alerces*, *Lago Puelo*, *Perito Moreno* and *Los Glaciares* National Parks; and also in different areas out of these parks.

Various campaigns of the Argentine Wildlife Foundation has provided valuable information about the distribution and abundance of the species. Nowadays, the National Park Administration is leading a *Huemul* Conservation Program.

Prints, excrement, marks on new shoots, reposing areas, hair, paths, browsed vegetation, smells, antlers, or bones are all remains that can be found and may give different clues. Analysing the length of the print, for example, researchers can categorise by sex and age. The *huemules* in *Los Glaciares* National Park are the most austral in the country. It is considered that the Patagonian icefield and the great lakes is surely a barrier they can't pass. The effect caused by cattle, wild and domesticated, has increased the isolation of this species (see page 5).

The commitment of some people in the area to protect the huemul is also noticed. A good example is the study funded by a firm owner of an estancia that includes *Lago Escondido*, in the South West of *Río Negro*. The results showed very few *huemules* lived in the area. In a town close to *Lago Puelo* it was declared a species of Municipal interest. The owners of *Chacra El Monje*, near the small town *El Hoyo*, mounted a wooden construction from where with a telescope and a bit of luck, it is possible to observe at a distance some on the *Cerro Pirque*.

The Pudú

The *Pudú* is an endemic species of the Valdivian and Magellan forests, adapted to move in dense cane fields (see page 58) and *ñirantales*. With a height of 35 to 40 cm and a weight of 9 to 11 kg, it is the smallest deer in the world.

Being small allows moving easily in the dense thicket forest. The *Pudú* marks its territory scratching branches with its antlers and leaving a smell on the small branches and leaves. It moves alone, or a male with a female and sometimes in small groups. The males reach their sexual maturity one year after birth and the females give one young. Staying in group in the dense and closed cane fields can have its complications. In groups they may be predated more easily than in an open environment.

The best strategy for this deer is to be alone and elusive. The *Puma* and the *Guiña* cat are its natural predators, but since decades dogs and man can be added to the list.

In open environments, the early

Female

Pudú

Male

95

detection of danger and the group defence are valuable advantages.

This may have been the case of the *Huemul* in the past (when they were more abundant) when they formed numerous groups in certain moments of the year. Records from the beginning of the century mention one hundred huemules in the area of *Lago Argentino*.

The foxes

The two species of foxes, whose distribution include the Andean Patagonian region, aren't exclusive inhabitants of the forests, but they relate with them.

The Red Fox or *Culpeo* prefers the heath and small forests of *Nothofagus*. The Patagonian Grey Fox prefer more open areas.

It is interesting to see the growth in size in both species as you go from north to south. Being bigger they reduce the exposed surface in relation with the volume; in this way keeping the heat better (a big cup of coffee takes longer than a small cup to get cold). This responds to a general rule valid for subspecies or geographic races of birds and mammals, also found for example in the guanaco and the puma.

The foxes are mainly carnivores, but both the Patagonian Grey Fox and the Red Fox eat fruits and can disperse the seeds (see page 31). If these fall in an adequate place they can germinate and form a new plant. But it has been proved also that the Patagonian Grey Fox can defecate seeds where the drying and predation will avoid their growth. We also know that the foxes predate some birds that are also dispersers.

With so many variables, the influence of the foxes as dispersers of seeds is difficult to estimate. But they do disperse seeds. Let's see characteristics of each.

The Red Fox or Culpeo

The Red Fox is distributed from the north of *Ecuador* to *Tierra del Fuego*, close to the Andean region. During the first decades of the XX century they may have started spreading towards the patagonian steppe as a result of the additional food supply due to the introduction of the European hare and the sheep.

Different subspecies are differentiated in the wide distribution and the fuegian subspecies is twice the size of the Small Grey Fox. They generally move alone when not in the reproductive season. They prefer to hunt in the dark, and they catch small rodents, eggs and bird chicks, lizards and frogs, diverse fruits and even fungi.

It makes nests in hollows and holes in trees or fallen tree trunks. After two months of gestation the female bears three to five puppies. While the mother breast feeds them, the male looks for food. The puppies are ready to start hunting at the age of two months.

Red fox

It is a witty hunter with stalking tactics or active hunting, capturing small mammals and birds and also eating insects and fruits. Its sensitive sense of smell helps it in this task, to such an extent that they are able to find food hidden by the pumas. They can also attack the sheep herds.

After two months of gestation, they bear two to four puppies. These remain protected in a tunnel by the mother who breast feeds them while the male finds food. They form new couples the following year. They have few natural predators.

The Patagonian Grey Fox

The Patagonian Grey Fox is distributed in the Andean-patagonian region and it was introduced by man in *Tierra del Fuego*. In general it's more abundant than the Red Fox. It moves alone and forms a couple through the end of winter and the beginning of spring.

Islands and foxes

In the year 1876 the warrah, a fox endemic to *Malvinas* (Falklands) islands, became extinct. A series of causes led to such a tragic end. Being inhabitant of the islands, the populations never were numerous (see page 19) and due to the lack of predators their attitude towards man was of curiosity and indifference. They became perfect targets for hunters and with the sheep farms, they were considered a harmful species.

The Guanaco

The *guanaco* has a wide distribution in South America but the most important populations reserve is in *Patagonia*. It adapts itself to a diversity of habitats, from extremes like the driest environment in the world, the *Atacama* Desert, to the damp fuegian forest. In Patagonia the steppe is its main habitat.

The social groups can be integrated by an adult male, the female and juveniles; groups of males; or groups of solitary males and females. After 11 months of gestation they give birth to a baby from 8 to 50 kg in weight.

During winter, especially in *Tierra del*

of the Shelknam (*Onas*) in the forest close to estancia Harberton, since the beginning of the XX century. The aborigines came from the fuegian steppes looking for guanacos to hunt. The estancias in northern Tierra del Fuego including thousands of sheep, started to move the *guanacos* and even the aborigines away.

In *Tierra del Fuego* it was determined that the main food of the *guanacos* all year round is the broom sedge type of grass (*Festuca sp*) and the *Deschampsia antarctica* (by the way this is one of the two species of flowering plants that grows in Subantartic islands and areas of northwestern Peninsula Antarctica). Among trees they prefer the *Lenga* and the *Ñire*, being the shoots and new leaves more palatable in spring.

The Huillín or Large River Otter

The *Huillín*, from the Mustelidae *family*, is a rare an endangered species. In *Argentina* three population nuclei are known and they are isolated from each other. The most important one has protection in *Nahuel Huapi* National Park. Another of recent discovery is found close to the Beagle Channel, in *Tierra del Fuego*, and the third one in Staten Island.

They have vespertine and nocturnal activity. There are records of big adults of up to 10 kg in weight and

Fuego, they move from the steppe to the nearby forests. They have been considered the native mammal with the most impact on the forest, and in certain areas they don't allow the regeneration of the *Lenga* and the *Ñire*. But the effects are less noticeable than in the past because the populations have decreased.

This species is an efficient forage gatherer as well as a tree browser; one or the other method may dominate according to the region. They can also change their diet in relation to the presence of sheep. If they have competition over pastures, they move towards the forest increasing the browsing.

In his book, *Uttermost Part of the Earth*, Lucas Bridges mentions the increase in frequency of appearance

110 cm in length. The waterproof hair, the web feet, and narines and ears with hermetic closure are adaptations to their aquatic habits, including diving.

Huillín

The studies of the *Nahuel Huapi* National Park population are the ones that provide the most information. Their main habitats are lakes, lagoons, rivers and streams with forest covering on the banks. Each male establishes his territory all along the banks, with two or three females that occupy smaller territories.

Freshwater crustaceans, and possibly clams, form part of their diet and they may travel long distances looking for food supply. In Tierra del Fuego and Staten Island, tide pools offer a good food supply.

They reproduce once a year and the females give birth in burrows on the banks protected by aquatic vegetation, and the presence of fallen logs may help (see page 32).

In the summer of 1982-83 biologists from the National Park Administration led a survey in the *Lanín, Nahuel Huapi, Lago Puelo* and *Los Alerces* National Park in order to know the distribution and population level.

There was evidence of their presence in the *Nahuel Huapi* lake and the water courses that run towards it, and in few places in the south of *Lanín* National Park. Another intense survey was held in the summer and beginning of autumn in 1995. Of 216 places visited, 77 showed evidence of valves of clams that accumulate where they eat, excrements and prints. Only one *Huillín* was seen.

Comparing the registers of both campaigns the conclusion was that the *Nahuel Huapi* and all its tributaries are key places in the conservation of the species. For its great area it seems to host a viable population. Lake *Traful* and the rivers and streams that run towards are a smaller area but also seem to have a stable population.

In rivers and streams the records on huillines are't frequent, although these courses are fundamental to connect the lakes. For example, in one of the last surveys they weren't detected in the *Gutiérrez* lake. A possible reason could be the increase of human presence in the area and a small dam on the *Gutiérrez* stream which connects this lake to the *Nahuel Huapi*.

On the other hand, there was no evidence of a negative influence of the mink (introduced species), although they share part of the diet as they both eat big crustaceans. However, more studies are needed to determine this.

The felines

The felines, besides the foxes, are the mammals that control the populations of rodents and other small mammals. Among them the *Guiña* is an endemic species of the Valdivian and Magellan forests with records in *Argentina* from the south-west of *Neuquén* to *Santa Cruz*. It has the size

Guiña Cat

of a domestic cat, with long fur and black spots. It lives on trees and is elusive and mimicking. Prey like the rodents are part of their diet but they can also hunt birds in the foliage.

The females give birth to five cubs and keep them in small caves or in fallen tree trunks, safe from the rapacious birds. Both parents feed them after the weaning.

The *Puma* uses the forest more as a refuge and raising area, while at night it searches for food in open areas where it can surprise its victims. In their wide distribution throughout the continent they include many subspecies. The one in *Patagonia* is the largest (see page 96) and it doesn't reach *Tierra del Fuego*. The diet is varied and adaptable to various conditions.

Studies in *Torres del Paine* National Park, concludes that 63 % of its diet is formed by guanacos, 20 % by european hares, 9 % by sheep, 4 % by birds such as the Upland Goose and the Lesser Rhea; and a 4 % by other

Puma

organisms. The hare hasn't been there more than 100 years since their introduction in the country, and the *Puma* has adapted well to predate it, a clear sign of its opportunism.

– • –

The Foreign Legion: introduced species

Continents drifting, the formation of mountain ranges, earthquakes and volcanoes, climatic changes. Some factors that since millions of years ago have been influencing the distribution and evolution of plants and animals. Multiple interactions of competition and co-operation have come up between organisms.

What happens when man introduces species in other natural environments, species that get there with a different historical background and interactions with different flora and fauna?
Some aren't successful but others may have certain advantage to develop in relation to the species of their "new world". Predators and parasites of the introduced species will be absent in the new land and decades may go by till the local predators affect the invading species. If they are pioneer species (see page 14), the expansion of the newly arrived may be much faster.

On the other hand, the isolated environments are less adapted to the introduction of alien species. For example, in the isolated New Zealand (see page 5) the bats are the only native mammals, and the introduction of the Red Deer (soon after 1850), among others, has caused a great impact. There the Red Deer has no natural predators that control its population and the vegetation is not adapted. A contrasting example is *Costa Rica* with an environment adapted to soften the effects of introduced species. Central America was used by groups of plants and animals that cross between North and South America since three million years ago. It has been a long time since far away organisms pass by or stay in the territory.

Our National Parks wish to protect the biodiversity as a major goal. The conservation of the interaction between organisms is fundamental. For this to be possible, it is important to avoid the introduction of alien species in protected areas.

Among the introduced species of acclimatized fauna, thirteen species of mammals, four of fish and two of birds have been identified in the Andean-Patagonian forests.
In the flora, only in the *Nahuel Huapi* National Park there are 145 species of alien plants. Some of the spanish

102

names of the most common and known are: *rosa mosqueta* (from *Neuquén* to *Chubut*), *lupines*, *margarita*, *dedalera* and *retama*.

The harmful effect of some species of alien fauna is known, but for others, more studies are needed. With the intentional or accidental introduction of species in areas where they don't belong, man has had a great influence over the place occupied by each species.

Nowadays, Darwin and Wallace would go nuts if they tried to determine why the species in the world have distributed in the way they did.

The fauna

Introduced trouts and salmons inhabit numerous Patagonian water courses. This is the case of the Brown Trout, the Rainbow Trout, the land-locked Salmon and Pacific Salmon.

Among birds, the California Quail was introduced in 1943 near *Lago Traful*, *Neuquén*. Today it is found in *Neuquén*, north of *Chubut* and various areas in *Chile*.

The introduced mammals produce the most visible harmful effects. The Muskrat is native from United States. In 1948 the Marine Minister introduced 225 individuals in *Tierra del Fuego* for the value of their skin. It spread quickly and caused great damage with their excavations or their eroding constructions. They are more controlled now a day.

The Beaver is native in the forests of conifers and *Populus sp* in the Northern Hemisphere, forests with rapid growth and recovery. Between 1945 and 1946 the Marine Minister introduced 25 couples in the Northeast of *Lago Fagnano* and *Río Claro, Tierra del Fuego*. They spread following the water courses. The

Beaver

Red deer

fuegian Forest is not adapted to replace the felling of trees for the construction of dams, nor the floods this produces.

Beavers prefer to establish themselves in medium size streams. They have a tendency to use the *Lenga* more than the *Guindo* and in general, trees with less than 10 cm in diameter. The older trees are less affected, at least from direct reasons, but floods caused by dams harm them. Recently, beavers were recorded in forests near *Punta Arenas*. This means that there

is a potential risk of expansion, and the consequent ecological damage.

The European Rabbit, a clear example of a colonising species (see page 14) may have been introduced in *Tierra del Fuego* in 1936. The American Mink, a Mustelidae, is native of United States. Introduced for the value of the fur, in the sixties some couples escaped from various mink farms (near *Futalaufquen, Chubut; Ñirihuau*, close to *Bariloche*; and other places in the region). They started to spread along the rivers and streams in the area of *Los Alerces* National Park, and northwards they invaded the basin of the lake *Nahuel Huapi*. They predate fishes, coypu, and different species of ducks, coots, and grebes. It was thought that the *Huillín* (see page 99) could also be affected, but no studies reveal this up to now.

The first introduction of the Red Deer in our forests is recorded between 1917 and 1922 in the province of *Neuquén*. Years have gone by, many deers have reproduced, and hundreds of hunters have hunted. Now a day there are 12,000 individuals in the *Lanín* National Park only, and they are still increasing.

Apart from being selected to hunt, activity that regulates the population number, observation excursions are being organised. It has been determined that the ecotone between the steppe and the forest, from *Neuquén* to *Río Negro*, is the most affected by the Red Deer.

The main difference of impact in the forest between the Red Deer and cattle is that the former is more selective.

The Deer has a greater impact on the Andean Cypress and less on not very palatable plants like the *Michay*, while the effects of cattle are uniform. On the other hand, they both produce clear inhibitions in the growth of the *Nothofagus*, the *Maqui* and the *Maitén*.

It has been proved that the intense browsing in the forest slowly increases spiny bushes (like *Berberis sp*), herbaceous plants and the relative abundance of alien plants.

An example of the flora

The Monterrey Pine

The *Monterrey* pine is native from the coast of California, where it is considered a relict species (see page 13) and only survives in five refuges. However, among forest trees, its plantations are the ones that cover the greatest surface in the world. Apart from *Chile*, they are important in New Zealand, Australia, South Africa, Spain, Portugal, and also in Brazil and Kenya.

It lives around 150 years in its natural region, while in plantations it lasts 25 years before being cut.

Its cultivation in *Chile* started in 1890, in the area of *Concepción*. In 1995 they had 1,2 million hectares with pine plantations. Most of them cover degraded lands which result from over a century of wheat fields, and more than 50,000 hectares of the pine plantations may have replaced native forests.

In the Andean-Patagonian area in *Argentina*, there are approximately 50,000 hectares of pines (not only *Monterrey*), mainly in the steppe.

One of the risks of monoculture is reduce the genetic variability (see page 19), and in consequence, the adaptation capacity. For example, a european moth may have crossed to *Chile* in 1985 severely affecting 50,000 hectares of the *Monterrey* Pine. As a biological control, a wasp (Orgilus obscurador) was introduced because the larvas eat the developing moth.

Other effects can occur on the lakes (see page 44) where the native forests were replaced directly by plantations; therefore the loss of diversity of the flora and fauna was very high. In a pine forest the records (visual counting) showed an abundance of 65 % of the bird species compared to the native forest (comparative study between the pine forest and the native forest in the X region in *Chile*).

We as part of Nature

"...we have to consider it a privilege to exist in an era of knowledge", I said in the introduction, and I really feel in this way.

Let's see other topics that knowledge provides us.
The birds are one group of creatures that we most admire and know. Since the XVI and XVII centuries, with the exploration of new worlds, records of the great diversity were made. The actual data indicates that since then, 171 species and subspecies of birds have become extinct. More than 90 % (155 species) lived on islands.

The Hawaiian Islands are a paradise in our perception, without any doubt. There, 24 birds' species and subspecies became extinct, more than in any other continent of the world. One of the main problems in Hawaii are the alien species. Such is the case of the wild pig, at present persecuted by hunters specially hired for their control.

Barro Colorado is an island (about 900 hectares) in Panama originated as a result of a dam construction at the beginning of the XX century. In 1923 it was declared a natural reserve, and dozens of biologists specialized in different topics have worked there. The Jaguar, the Puma and big eagles have disappeared long ago. Since the reserve creation, 22 % of the bird species aren't registered there.

Why? Basically because they are islands. In many parts of the book I mention how isolation affects the forms of life.

Researchers consider that not only species become extinct. In the Earth there are many ecological and evolutionary processes that come to an end. Also, the rhythm of loss of species and ecosystems will be greater than the advance of researchers to know which the conservation priorities are. To diminish the uncertainty, it is considered a priority to create protected areas that represent most of the ecosystems.

Our Southern Beech Forests are isolated including many endemic groups of flora and fauna. Of course, the surface of the forests is much greater than the islands mention and they are surrounded by earth not water.
Also we must consider that man influence has been different in each case. According to Laclau (1997), half of our remaining forests are in a bad biological status. The selective extraction of the best trees in the wood industry, and cattle on the pastures of new shoots are two very important causes.

With the modification and destruction of the surroundings, our natural environments are looking more like I-S-L-A-N-D-S.
And to globalise the concept, this is happening in the whole world.

If we consider not only the Southern Forests as a whole, but the natural reserves that protect them, National Parks standing out, the risks of being islands become more evident with the modifications of the surroundings. For example, for the *Nahuel Huapi* National Park it is considered that 30 to 40 % of the area has been affected by cattle in different sorts of degree.

Also, it is important to consider the diversity of the habitat, not only the size of the area protected. For example *Los Glaciares* National Park covers 600,000 ha, and only 13 % of them are forests.

We, the human species, have a unique genetic inheritance that allows us a type of evolution not comparable with other forms of life. There is no evidence of changes in our body or brain in the last 100,000 years. But our cultural changes have been immense. With our capacity to think, we can accumulate and transmit information from generation to generation. And we are conscious of this.
During more than 99 % of our history, the hunter-collector ancestors lived in small groups, in intimate contact with other organisms. The first human civilisations appeared only 50,000 years ago. Only 300 years ago, the first books were printed, and less than two decades since computers became so popular.
Humanity has accumulated an immensity of knowledge. But in spite of the fact that we conscientiously can control our destiny, evidence shows that the world we live in has L-I-M-I-T-S. We have come upon a unique situation in our short history, where the increase in population and the terrible inequalities have a lot to do. Trying to value Natural Resources from the economic point of view

and our activity in relation to them is a growing and needed tendency. It is a key concept that the protection of the environment must be centred in the sustainable use.

However, there is a concept that goes further and I think it is important to assimilate: We aren't owners of the world; we are simply part of it. If we include time, let's say from the origin of life, we must admit that as a species we have just arrived. Accepting and assimilating deeply this concept, surely implies a change in attitude.
It would be good that each one of us experienced that living on this planet is wonderful. To see, taste, smell, and feel the grandiosity of Nature. Our senses will receive incredible stimuli in this environment.

Also, with our great capacity to T-H-I-N-K, let's assimilate some of the topics presented in these pages.

To finish, a thought from writer Leo Tolstoy (1828-1910):
"Nature... is a friend you will never lose until death - and even when you die, you disappear into nature..."

Bibliography

- Aniya, M. y P. Skvarca. 1992. Characteristics and variations of Upsala and Moreno glaciers, southern Patagonia. Bulletin of Glacier Research 10: 39-53.

- Administración de Parques Nacionales, 1991. Plan General de manejo (documento preliminar para trabajo y discusión). Parque Nacional Los Glaciares, Delegación Técnica del Sur, S.C. de Bariloche.

- Arias, D.E. 1999. Todos los fuegos, el fuego. Revista Vida Silvestre Nº 67, Bs. As.

- Armesto, J.J., I. Casassa, O. Dollenz. 1992. Age structure and dynamics of Patagonian beech forests in Torres del Paine National Park, Chile. Vegetatio 98: 13-22.

- Armesto, J.J. C. Villagran, M.T. Arroyo, (editores) 1997. Ecología de los bosques nativos de Chile. 477 p. Editorial Universitaria, Santiago de Chile.

- Arroyo, M.T., C. Donoso, R.E. Murúa, E.E. Pisano, R.P. Schlatter, I.A. Serey. 1996. Toward an ecologically sustainable forestry project. Protecting Biodiversity and Ecosystem processes in the Río Cóndor Project, Tierra del Fuego. 253 p. Departamento de Investigación y Desarrollo, Universidad de Chile.

- Axelrod, D.I., M.T. Kalin Arroyo, P.H. Raven. 1991. Historical development of temperate vegetation in the Americas. Revista Chilena de Historia Natural 64: 413-446.

- Beccaceci, M., 1998. Patagonia Natural, Pangaea. Saint Paul, Minnesota.

- Bertonatti C., 1999. Culebra Valdiviana, Vida Silvestre Nº 68, Bs. As.

- Bridges, E.L., 1951. Uttermost part of the World. Readers Union Hodder and Stoughton, London.

- Bustamante, R.O, J.A. Simonetti, J.E. Mella. 1992. Are foxes legiti-mate and efficient seed dispersers ? A field test. Acta Oecologica 13 (2), 203-208.

- Canevari, M., P. Canevari, G.R. Carrizo, G. Harris, J. Rodriguez Mata, R.J. Straneck, 1991. Nueva Guía de las Aves Argentinas, Tomo II. Fundación Acindar. Bs. As.

- Carrillo R., L. Cerda. 1987. Zoofitófagos en Nothofagus chilenos. Bosque: 8 (2): 99-103.

- Chebez, J.C. 1994. Los que se van. Especies argentinas en peligro.

Editorial Albatros, Buenos Aires.

• Chebez, J.C. y A. Bosso. 1992.
Un curioso comportamiento
alimentario del Caburé Grande
(Glaucidium nanum). Rev. Nuestras
Aves IX (26): 26-27. AOP, Bs. As.

• Chehebar, C. y E. Ramilo, 1989.
Fauna del Parque Nacional Nahuel
Huapi, Gral. Roca, Rio Negro.

• Cei, J.M. 1980.
Amphibians of Argentina. Monitore
Zoologico Italiano (N.S.) Monogr. 2.

• Clapp R.A. 1995.
The Unnatural History of the
Monterey Pine. The Geographical
Review. Volume 85, N 1, 1-19.

• Collias, N.E. & E.C. Collias.1984.
Nest Building and Bird Behavior.
Princeton University Press, Princeton.

• Corporacion Forestal Nacional, 1991.
El Guanaco. Boletín Técnico Nº 47:
1-35, Santiago de Chile.

• Correa, A., J.J. Armesto,
R. Schlatter, J.C. Rozzi. 1990.
La dieta del Chucao (Scelorchilus
rubecula), un Pas-seriforme terrícola
endémico del bosque templado
húmedo de Sudamérica austral.
Rev. Chilena de Historia Natural
63: 197,-202.

• Dimitri, 1974.
Pequeña Flora Ilustrada de los
Parques Nacionales Andino-
Patagónicos. Anales de Parques
Nacionales, Tomo XIII: 1-122,
Buenos Aires.

• Donoso C., V. Sandoval, R. Grez,
J. Rodriguez,. 1993.
Dynamycs of Fitzroya cupressoides
forests in Southern Chile. Journal of
Vegetation Science 4: 303-312.

• Erize, F. 1993.
El Gran Libro de la Naturaleza
Argentina. Rev. Gente,
Edit. Atlántida, Buenos Aires.

• Erize, F., M. Canevari, P. Canevari,
G. Costa, M. Rumboll (1981) 1995.
Los Parques Nacionales de la
Argentina y otras de sus áreas
naturales. Incafo - Ed. El Ateneo.

• Fjeldsa, J. & N. Krabbe. 1990.
Birds of the High Andes.
Zoologi-cal Museum,
University of Copenhagen.

• Fraga, R.M., A.E. Ruffini,
D. Grigera. 1997. Interacciones
entre el Picaflor Rubí Sephanoides
sephanoides y plantas del Bosque
Subantártico en el Parque Nacional
Nahuel Huapi, Argentina.
Hornero 14: 224-234.

• Franklin, W.L. 1982.
Biology, ecology and relationship to

man of the south American Camelids. Special Publication Pymatuning Laboratory of Ecology, N 6:457-489.

Gamundí, I.J. & E. Horak, 1995. Fungi of the Andean-Patagonian Forests. Field Guide to the Identification of the most common and atracctive fungi. Vazquez Mazzini Editores, Buenos Aires.

Goodall, R.N.P. 1979. Tierra del Fuego. Ediciones Shana-maiim, Ushuaia.

Gould, S.J. 1991. Bully for Brontosaurus. 540 p. Penguin Books, London.

Harper,J.L., P.H. Lovell, K.G. Moore. 1970. The shapes and sizes of seeds. Annual Review of Ecology and Systematics, 1: 327-356.

Heinonen Fortabat, S. y J.C. Chebez, 1997. Los Mamíferos de los Parques Nacionales de la Argentina. Monogr. (14), edit L.O.L.A., Bs. As.

Hill, R.S. 1992. Nothofagus: Evolution from a Southern Perspective. Tree, Vol. 7, Nº 6, 190-194.

Hoffmann, A.E. 1995. Flora Silvestre de Chile, zona araucana. 257 p. Ediciones Fundación Claudio Gay, Santiago de Chile.

Howe, H.F., J. Smallwood. 1982. Ecology of seed dispersal. Annual Rev. Ecol. Syst. 13:201-228.

Jacome, L. 1998. Liberación de Cóndores. De vuelta en casa. Naturaleza y Conservación Nº 3, AOP, Bs. As.

Jaksic, F.A. 1997. Ecología de los Vertebrados de Chile. 262 p. Ediciones Universitad Católica de Chile, Santiago de Chile.

Jaksic, F.M., J.L. Yanez y J.R. Rau, 1983. Trophic relations of the southernmost populations of Dusicyon in Chile. J. Mammology, 64 (4): 693-697.

Janzen, D.H. 1983. No park is an island: increase in interference from outside as park size decreases, Oikos 41: 402-410.

Jimenez J.E., F.A. Jaksic, 1990. Historia Natural del Aguila Geranoaetus melanoleucus: una revisión. El Hornero, Vol. 13, Número 2: 97-110, Buenos Aires.

Johnson, H. 1987. El Bosque, Fauna, Flora y recursos económicos del bosque mundial. 223 p. Editorial Blume, Barcelona.

Johnson, W.E. 1992. Patagonia's Little Foxes. Natural History. april: 26-31.

- Johnson, W.E., W.L. Franklin, J.A. Iriarte. 1990. The mammalian fauna of the northern Chilean Patagonia: a biogeographical dilemma. Mammalia, t. 54, Nº 3 457-467.

- Johnson, W.E., W.L. Franklin, J.A. Iriarte. 1994. Conservation implications of South American Grey Fox socioecology in the Patagonia of Southern Chile. Vida Silvestre Neotropical 3 (1):16-23.

- Laclau, P. 1997. Los Ecosistemas Forestales y el Hombre en el sur de Chile y Argentina. Boletín Técnico Nº 34. F.V.S.A., Bs. As.

- López, Barry. 1987. Arctic Dreams, 417 p, Bantam Books.

- Margalef, R. 1986. Ecología. Ediciones Omega S.A., Barcelona.

- Marini, M.A., R.B. Cavalcanti. 1998. Frugivory by Elaenia Flycatchers. Hornero 15: 47-50, Bs. As.

- Massoia, E y J.C. Chebez, 1993. Mamíferos Silvestres del Archipiélago Fueguino. Edit. L.O.L.A., Bs. As.

- Mc Ewan, C., L.A. Borrero, A. Prieto, (editors) 1997. Patagonia, Natural History, Prehistory and Ethnography at the Uttermost End of the Earth. 200 p. The Trusters of the British Museum, London.

- Moreno, D.I., 1993. Ciervos Autóctonos de la República Argentina. Boletín Técnico Nº 17, 39 p. F.V.S.A., Buenos Aires.

- Narosky, T. & D. Yzurieta. 1988. Guía para la identificación de las Aves de la Argentina & Uruguay. Vazquez Mazzini Editores, Bs. As.

- Naruse, R. y M. Aniya, 1992. Outline of Glacier Research Project in Patagonia. Bulletin of Glacier Research 10: 31-38.

- Novaro, A.J., 1997. Pseudolopex culpaeus. Mammalian species, Nº 558, 1-8. American Society of Mammalogists.

- Nowak, R.M. 1991. Walker's Mammals of the World. 5º Edition. Vol II. The Johns Hopkins University Press, Baltimore and London.

- Pearson, O.P., A.K. Pearson 1982. Ecology and Biogeo-graphy of the Southern Rainforests of Argentina. Special Publica-tion Pymatuning Laboratory of Ecology. N 6: 129-142.

- Pelt, J.M. 1985. Las Plantas. Biblioteca Científica Salvat, Barcelona.

- Peña, L.E., 1988. Introducción a los insectos de Chile. Editorial Universitaria, Santiago de Chile.

- Perrins, C.M., A.L. Middleton (ed) 1998. The Encyclopedia of Birds. 447 p. Facts on File, Inc. New York.

- Porro G. y C. Chebehar, 1995. Monitoreo de la distribución del Huillin (Lontra provocax) en el Parque Nacional Nahuel Huapi, Argentina. Delegación Técnica Regional Patagonia, APN, S.C. de Bariloche.

- Putman, R. 1988.The Natural History of Deer. 191 p. Cornwell University Press, Ithaca, New York.

- Quammen, D. 1996. The Song of the Dodo. Island Biogeography in an Age of Extinctions. 702 p. Touchstone, New York.

- Ramirez, C.G. 1987. El género Nothofagus y su importancia en Chile. Bosque 8 (2) 71-76.

- Redon, J. 1985. Líquenes antárticos. Instituto Antártico Chileno, Santiago de Chile.

- Regal, P.J. 1982. Pollination by wind and animals: Ecology of Geographic Patterns. Ann. Rev. Ecol. Syst. 13: 497-524.

- Riveros, M.G., A.M. Humana, D. Lanfranco. 1991. Actividad de los polinizadores en el Parque Nacional Puyehue, X Region, Chile.

- Medio Ambiente, 11 (2):5-12.

- Roberts, W.M. 1995. Hummingbird licking behavior and the energe-tics of nectar feeding. The Auk 112 (2) 456-463.

- Russo, R.M., P.G. Silver. 1995. The Andes' Deep Origins. Natural History, february: 53-58.

- Santos Biloni, J. 1990. Arboles autóctonos argentinos. Tipográfica Editora Argentina, Buenos Aires.

- Serret, A. y F. Borghiani, 1996. Avances en el conocimiento del huemul en el Seno Moyano, Parque Nacional Los Glaciares, Boletín Técnico Nº 32 de la FVSA, Bs. As.

- Short, L.L. 1970. The habits and relationships of the Magellanic Wood-pecker. The Wilson Bulletin, Vol 82, Nº 2.

- Simpson, G., 1982. The Book of Darwin. Washington Square Press, New York.

- Smith-Ramirez, C., J.J. Armesto. 1994. Flowering and fruiting patterns in the temperate rainforest of Chiloe, Chile-ecologies and climatic constraints. Journal of Ecology, 82, 353-365.

- Stebbins, R.C., N.W. Cohen. 1995. A Natural History of Amphibians.

316 p. Princeton University Press, Princeton.

- Tell, G., Izaguirre, R., Quintana R.D., 1997. Flora y Fauna Patagónicas. Ed Caleuche. S.C. de Bariloche.

- Thompson, J.N., M.F. Willson. 1979. Evolution of Temperate fruit-bird interactions: phenological strategies. Evolution, 33 (3): 973-982.

- Tudge, C. 1996. The Time before History. Scribner, New York.

- Veblen, T.T. 1979. Structure and dynamics of Nothofagus forests near timberline in south central Chile. Ecology 60 (5) 937-945.

- Veblen, T.T., D.H. Ashton, F.M. Schegel, A.T. Veblen, 1978. Influencia del estrato arbóreo sobre los estratosinferiores en un bosque mixto, perenne-caducifolio de Antillanca, Osorno, Chile. Bosque Vol 2, Nº 2: 88-104.

- Veblen T.T.; M. Mermoz, C. Martin, T. Kitzberger. 1992. Ecological impacts of introduced animals in Nahuel Huapi National Park, Argentina. Conservation Biology, vol 6, Nº 1: 71-83.

- Veblen, T.T., M. Mermoz, C. Martin, E. Ramilo. 1989. Effects of exotic deer on forest regeneration and composition in Northern Patagonia. Journal of Applied Ecology 26: 711-724.

- Veblen, T.T., F.M. Schegel.1982. Reseña ecológica de los bos-ques del sur de Chile. Bosque (4) 2: 73-115

- Vidoz, F. 1985. Los Huemules de lago Escondido, Informe Preliminar. Asociación Ornitológica Cuenca del Puelo, Río Negro.

- Vuilleumer, F. 1985. Forests Birds of Patagonia: Ecological geography, speciation, endemism, and faunal history. Ornithological Monographs Nº 36: 255-304.

- Whitehead, D.R. 1969. Wind Pollination in the Angiosperms: evolutionary and environmental considerations. Evolution 23: 28-35.

- Willson, M.F. 1991. Dispersal of seeds by frugivorous animals in temperate forests. Revista Chilena de Historia Natural. 64: 537-554.

- Willson, M.F., T.L. De Santo. 1994. Avian Communities of Fragmented South-Temperate Rainforests in Chile. Conservation Biology, Vol 8, Nº 2, 508-520.

Our National Parks

The National Parks of Argentina originated in 1903 when Francisco Pascacio Moreno donated 7,500 ha of his property in the region which would later be the Nahuel Huapi National Park. This donation was accepted by the National Government in 1904, forming the initial core of the Park, which was extended to 43,000 ha in 1907, and completed in 1922 with a total surface of 785,000 ha.

In the meantime, thanks to the negotiations done by Carlos Thays, the Argentine Government bought 75,000 ha in Iguazú, to form a National Park and a Military colony.

The consolidation of these two visionary men only happened in 1934 with the promulgation of the first National Park's law, elaborated by Dr. Ezequiel Bustillo. Three years later, other areas were added to these parks: Lanín, Los Alerces, Perito Moreno and Los Glaciares.

This initial stage was characterized by a great impulse. Great investments in equipment and infrastructure aiming mainly at the development of tourism. This policy which was characterized by the protection of the areas of great beauty, changed with time. Argentina is a country with a great diversity of environments, many unique or shared in a small area with neighboring countries. But a high percentage of these environments are not represented, or at least not enough, in the national protected areas.

The great agro-industrial development and the demographic growth have lead to dramatic modifications in all natural environments, with the loss of genetic variability. This not only means its potential use, but also, the loss of the origin of the roots and culture of Argentina.

That is why the Administración de Parques Nacionales has made a great effort in the concretion of new areas which represent and protect the native biological diversity of Argentina. The thirty three areas protected today, many recently created, preserve samples of many of these environments. Never-the-less, the total surface of these areas is hardly more than 1 % of the total surface of Argentina. There are some biomes which are not represented, and several national parks that are too small to ensure protection in the long run.

There is still a lot to do.

Marcelo Canevari
Administración de Parques Nacionales

THE NATIONAL PARKS IN THE PATAGONIAN FORESTS

The National Parks are areas designated by the State for protecting nature. The Parks generally are large areas, and preferably with no or very little modifications originated in human activities, and which harbor the species of flora and fauna characteristic of an ecological region, including in some cases, noteworthy landscapes.

The patagonian forest has a very special significance for nature conservation in Argentina, because it was in this region that the argentinian system of National Parks was born –from the donation of 7,500 hectares made by Francisco Pascasio Moreno in 1903, in the Puerto Blest area –at the heart of what is today the Nahuel Huapi National Park.

Since then, the andean-patagonian forest has achieved an important level of protection through the creation of Lanín, Nahuel Huapi, Arrayanes, Lago Puelo, Los Alerces, Perito Moreno, Los Glaciares and Tierra del Fuego National Parks. This set of Parks makes for a total of approximately 2,000,000 hectares of protected land.

Due to their contact with protected areas in Chile and with other non-federal protected areas in Argentina, the effective size of some parks is considerably augmented. For example, Lanín, Nahuel Huapi and Arrayanes National Parks are contiguous and also adjoin Llao-llao Municipal Park and the provincial Limay Protected Landscape, as well as Villarrica National Reserve, and Villarrica, Pérez Rosales and Puyehue National Parks in Chile. Together, these comprise a continuous, though irregularly shaped, protected area of 1,628,215 ha. Similarly, Los Glaciares National Park and Península Magallanes Provincial Reserve in Argentina, together with Torres del Paine and Bernardo O'Higgins National Parks in Chile, make up a large continuous protected area of 4, 474, 242 ha.

The significant size of several parks or of "park complexes" helps in the conservation of ecological processes and of disturbance patterns at multiple scales.

These protected areas make possible to conserve:

• representative samples of the latitudinal variation of the patagonian or subantarctic forest, which includes valuable and diverse forest communities, such as the araucaria, roble-pellín (a species of deciduous southern beech), raulí (another deciduous southern beech), ingressions of valdivian temperate rain forest, cypress forests, coihue (an evergreen southern beech), alerce, and the southern forests of guindo or Magallanes coihue (another evergreen southern beech). The system provides a representation of the diversity of the southern-beeches.

• the headwaters of some of the most important patagonian watersheds, such is the case of rivers Negro and Santa Cruz. This protection is an insurance for the viability of important hydroenergetic infrastructure and has a fundamental regulating role for the development of regional economies.

• some of the most spectacular wild landscapes of Argentina, and many beautiful sites which attract thousands of visitors.

• valuable expressions of the cultural and archaeological heritage –e.g. wall paintings or rock shelters of ancient peoples.

The complex history of human use and occupation of the andean patagonian region, is reflected also in the National Parks. As a consequence, these National Parks and National Reserves have –along with strict conservation areas virtually without human activity– other portions with significant services for tourism, or with rural activities (such as areas inhabited by mapuche communities or rural settlers who are successors of former colonists; and even some private properties pre-existing at the moment of creation of Lanín and Nahuel Huapi National Parks.

The protection of these forests has already been fructiferous, not only in ecological but also in economic terms, because the forest and the landscape are indispensable for tourism, the central activity for regional development. Fortunately, other protected areas –provincial and municipal– are adding to the National Parks, and nature conservation is becoming a shared goal of all the communities inhabiting the andean patagonian region.

Administración de Parques Nacionales
Delegación Regional Patagonia

Birds in PATAGONIA

Andean Condor, by Aldo Chiappe

Almost 1.000 species of birds are distributed through forests, desserts, pampas, high Andes, seacoasts and other natural areas of Argentina. 80 of them are endangered species, including endemic species in Patagonia as the Austral Rail, the Hooded Grebe and the Striated Caracara.

The Andean Forest, the Patagonian steppes, and the seacoast in Patagonia need urgent conservation measures in order to preserve their flora and fauna and ecological processes, and also to allow future generations to find joy in them.

AVES ARGENTINAS/AOP works hard in order to connect our people with the wildlife of this vast and overwhelming region. We organized nature tours every summer to different areas, we produce publications to promote the conservation of species as the Andean Condor, and we have active participation in meetings with specialists to discuss the conservation strategies of our Patagonian natural resources, among other activities.

AVES ARGENTINAS/AOP is a non profit organization that since 1916 works in the country for the study and conservation of birds and their natural habitats.

25 de mayo 749 º2 "6" - (C1002BO) Buenos Aires, Argentina
(54 11) 4312-8958/1015/2284 - info@avesargentinas.org.ar
www.avesargentinas.org.ar

AVES ARGENTINAS
Asociación Ornitológica del Plata

The Fundación Vida Silvestre Argentina in Patagonia

FUNDACION VIDA SILVESTRE ARGENTINA

The Fundación Vida Silvestre Argentina FVSA works to preserve the diversity of life and to build a future where humanity can live in harmony with nature.

From its origin in 1977, the FVSA has been performing an intense activity in Patagonia to make reality its institutional goals:

- Preserve the biological diversity: developing conservation projects for endangered species in Patagonia as the Southern Right Whale, the Hooded Grebe, the Huemul deer and the Pudú deer.
- Control environmental policies and cooperate with environmental planning: for example, producing an Inform with the FVSA position related to the sustainable use of the forest in Tierra del Fuego; working with other institutions in a management strategy for the temperate forests in Southern Argentina and Chile; beeing a key institution for the creation of Monte León, the first coastal National Park in Argentina.
- Education: educational campaigns in Los Alerces, Lanín and Nahuel Huapi national parks; environmental education programs for teachers from Puerto Madryn, Comodoro Rivadavia, Puerto Deseado, San Martín de los Andes and Esquel; educational posters from natural environments, etc.
- Inform: Publications, as the *Guía de Reconocimiento de Cetáceos del Mar Argentino*, and eighteen technical bulletins related to Patagonian subjects.

One of the natural communities with greater biodiversity in the Andean Patagonian Forest is the Valdivian Forest. The Fundación Vida Silvestre Argentina inaugurated in 1999 a Regional office in San Carlos de Bariloche to develop a conservation global vision for the area. To optimize fires prevention systems, protected native endangered species, helps regulate urban development, manage wild and domestic cattle in natural environments, and control exotic species, are some of the conservation actions that the FVSA propose to develop from its Regional Office.

The Patagonian Forest needs us all. Help us to protect it.
Programa Bosque Andino Patagónico Selva Valdiviana CC 794 (8400) Bariloche, Río Negro, Argentina 0054-2944422731/429862. Main Office: Defensa 251 6to K. (C1065AAC) Buenos Aires Argentina 0054-11-4331-3631

IGUAZÚ
The LAWS of the JUNGLE

Santiago G. de la Vega
Illustrations: Gustavo R. Carrizo

Contents

Fauna

CONTACTO
SILVESTRE
ediciones

Flora and Fauna: List of species

1- Include in the book; 2- include in the cover; (e)- Exotic species.

Flora

Alerce – *Fitzroya cupressoides*   1, 2
Arrayán – *Myrceugenella apiculata*   1, 2
Avellano – *Gevuina avellana*   1
Canelo – *Drimys winteri*   1
Andean Cypress –
   Austrocedrus chilensis   1
Ciprés de las Guaytecas –
   Pilgerodendron uviferum   1, 2
Coihue – *Nothofagus dombeyi*   1, 2
Guindo – *Nothofagus betuloides*   1
Lenga – *Nothofagus pumilio*   1, 2
Maitén – *Maytenus boaria*   1
Maniú hembra –
Saxegothaea conspicua   1, 2
Maniú macho –
Podocarpus nibigena   1
Monterrey Pine – *Pinus radiata*   (e) 1
Ñire – *Nothofagus antarctica*   1
Pehuén – *Araucaria araucana*   1
Radal – *Lomatia hirsuta*   1
Raulí – *Nothofagus nervosa*   1, 2
Roble Pellín – *Nothofagus oblicua*   1
Sauco del Diablo –
   Pseudopanax laetevireus   1
Tineo – *Weinmannia trichosperma*   2

Calafate – *Berberis buxifolia*   1, 2
Colihue cane – *Chusquea culeou*   1, 2
Chaura– *Pernettya mucronata*   1
Chilco – *Fuchsia magellanica*   1, 2
Corcolén – *Azara lanceolata*   1
Dedalera – *Digitalis purpurea*   (e) 1
Fuinque – *Lomatia ferruginea*   1
Maqui – *Aristotelia maqui*   1

Michay – *Berberis darwinii*   1
Mutilla – *Empetrum rubrum*   1
Notro – *Embothrium coccineum*   1
Pangue o nalca – *Gunnera chilensis*   1, 2
Parrilla – *Ribes magellanicum*   1
Rosa Mosqueta – *Ribes rubiginosa* (e) 1
Siete Camisas – *Escallonia rubra*   1

Amancay – *Alstroemeria aurantiaca* 1, 2
Botellita – *Mitraria coccinea*   1, 2
Estrellita – *Asteranthera ovata*   1, 2
Frutilla – *Fragaria chiloensis*   2
Lágrima de cascada – *Ourisia alpina*   2
Llao-llao – *Cyttaria darwini*   1, 2
Mimulus – *Mimulus luteus*   2
Mutisia – *Mutisia decurrens*   1
Pil-pil Voqui –
   Campsidium valdivianum   1, 2
Myzodendron –
   Myzodendron punctulatum   1, 2
Palmerilla –
   Dicranopterix quadripartita   2
Old's man beard – *Usnea sp.*   1, 2
Quintral – *Tristerix tetrandus*   1
Taique – *Desfontainea spinosa*   2
Topa-topa – *Calceolaria crenatifolia*   2

Fauna

Caballito – *Aegorhinus vitulus*
   (Curculionidae)   2
Bumble bee – *Bombus sp.*   1
Bagre aterciopelado –
   Diplomystes viedmensis   1
Bagre de los torrentes –

Hatcheria macraei 1

Pejerrey patagónico –
Odontesthes microlepidotus 1

Puyenes – *Galaxias sp.* 1

Salmón Encerrado –
Salmo salar sebazo (e) 1

Rainbow trout –
Oncorhynchus mykiss (e) 1

Trucha de Arroyo –
Salvelinus fontinalis 1

Brown trout – *Salmo trutta* (e) 1

Darwin's Frog –
Rhinoderma darwini 1, 2

Rana de Challhuaco –
Atelognathus nitoi 1

Rana palmada de arroyo –
Alsodes gargola 1

Rana verde austral –
Hylorina sylvatica 2

Sapito cuatro ojos –
Pleurodema thaui 2

Sapo Andino – *Bufo spinolosus* 1

Sapo del Bosque – *Bufo variegatus* 1, 2

Culebra andina –
Tachymenis peruviana 2

Lagartija de cabeza verde –
Liolaemus chilensis 1

Andean Condor – *Vultur gryphus* 1

Andean Flicker – *Colaptes pitius* 1

Austral Parakeet –
Enicognathus ferrugineus 1, 2

Austral Pigmy Owl – *Glaucidium nanum* 1, 2

Austral Thrush –
Turdus falcklandii 1, 2

Black-faced Ibis –

Theristicus melanopis 2

Bicolored Hawk – *Accipiter bicolor* 1, 2

Black-chested Buzzard tagle –
Geranoaetus melanoleucus 1

Black-throated Huet-huet –
Pteroptochos tarnii 1, 2

California Quail –
Lophortyx californica (e) 1, 2

Chilean Pigeon –
Columba araucana 1, 2

Chimango Caracara –
Milvago chimango 1

Chucao Tapaculo –
Scelorchilus rubecula 1, 2

Crested Caracara –
Polyborus plancus 1

Green-backed Firecrown –
Sephanoides sephanoides 1

Great Grebe – *Podiceps major* 1, 2

Imperial Cormorant –
Phalacrocorax atriceps 1

Lesser Rhea – *Pterocnemia pennata* 1

Magellanic Woodpecker –
Campephilus magellanicus 1, 2

Ñacurutú – *Bubo virginianus* 1

Patagonian Sierra Finch –
Phrygilus patagonicus 2

Rufous-collared Sparrow –
Zonotrichia capensis 1

Silvery Grebe – *Podiceps occipitalis* 1

Slender-billed Conure –
Enicognathus leptorhynchus 1

Striped Woodpecker –
Picoides lignarius · 1, 2

Thorn–tailed Rayadito –
Aphrastura spinicaudata 1, 2

Torrent Duck –
Merganetta armata 1, 2

Upland Goose – *Cloephaga picta* 1

White-crested Elaenia –
  Elaenia albiceps 1
White-throated Caracara –
  Polyborus albogularis 1
White-throated Treerunner –
  Pygarrhichas albogularis 1
White-tufted Grebe –
  Podiceps rolland 1

Beaver – *Castor canadensis* (e) 1
Red Deer – *Cerphus elaphus* (e) 1
Colilargo austral –
  Oligoryzomys longicaudatus 2
Coypu – *Myocastor coypus* 1
European Rabbit –
  Oryctolagus cuniculus (e) 2
Guanaco – *Lama guanicoe* 1
Guiña cat – *Oncifelis guigna* 1, 2
Huemul deer –
  Hippocamelus bisulcus 1, 2
Huillín – *Lontra provocax* 1, 2
Mink – *Mustela vison* (e) 1

Monito de Monte –
  Dromiciops gliroides 1, 2
Murciélago Colorado –
  Lasiurus varius 2
Murciélago patagón –
  Myotis chiloensis
Pudú deer – *Pudu pudu* 1, 2
Puma – *Felis concolor* 1
Rata topo valdivinana –
  Geoxus valdivianus 2
Ratón de oreja negra –
  Irenomys tarsalis 2
Ratón hocico bayo –
  Abrothrix xanthorhinus 2
Social Tuco-tuco –
  Ctenomys sociabilis 1
Red fox – *Lycalopex culpaeus* 1
Patagonian grey fox –
  Lycalopex gymnocereus 1
Patagonian hog-nosed skunk –
  Conepatus humboldtii 1
Warrah or Falkland Island wolf –
  Dusicyon australis 1

Many people contributed generously offering varied knowledge and skills to the production of this book.

Gustavo R. Carrizo is a main contributor as the author of the illustrations.
The Argentina Wildlife Foundation offered the illustration from the patagonian forest by Aldo Chiappe to use in the cover. Carlos Fernández Balboa makes it possible.
Andrés Bosso, Marcelo Canevari, Claudio Chehébar, and Juan Carlos Chebez make different suggestions, and assist with corrections on different technical and conceptual matters.
Mónica Mermoz and Eduardo Ramilo read portions of the text and offered technical corrections.
Alejandro Serret contributes with the subjects of the Huemul deer.

Once more, the bibliography has been invaluable as a raw material to shape these pages. The authors of many of the publications are researchers and conservationists from Argentina and Chile with many years devoted to the study and conservation of the Andean Patagonian forest. Their works represent indispensable tools to develop proper diagnosis and conservation measures.

My father Carlos Alberto and my brother Diego make me suggestions from their visitor point of view.

Also thanks to Matt Von Konrat

Verónica Martorell makes most of the graphic design, and Jorge García design the cover.

To all of them my deep gratitude,

Santiago G. de la Vega

127

Cover illustration latin names:
see pages 123-125

sdelavega@contactosilvestre.com.ar

Distribution of trees in the Southern Beech Forests

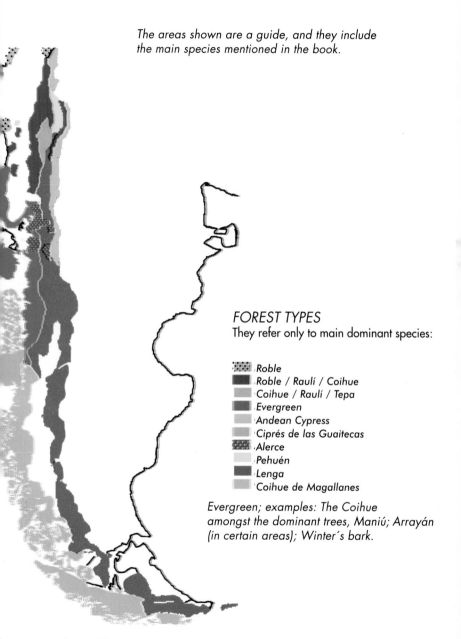

The areas shown are a guide, and they include the main species mentioned in the book.

FOREST TYPES
They refer only to main dominant species:

- Roble
- Roble / Raulí / Coihue
- Coihue / Raulí / Tepa
- Evergreen
- Andean Cypress
- Ciprés de las Guaitecas
- Alerce
- Pehuén
- Lenga
- Coihue de Magallanes

Evergreen; examples: The Coihue amongst the dominant trees, Maniú; Arrayán (in certain areas); Winter´s bark.

SOURCE: Laclau, Pablo 1997. Los Ecosistemas Forestales y el Hombre en el sur de Chile y Argentina. Boletín Tecnico N 34. FVSA (with adaptations)

Pehuén

Alerce

Andean Cypress

Ciprés de las Guaytecas

Lenga

Ñire

Guindo

Coihue

Raulí

Growing under the trees: the understory - page 57

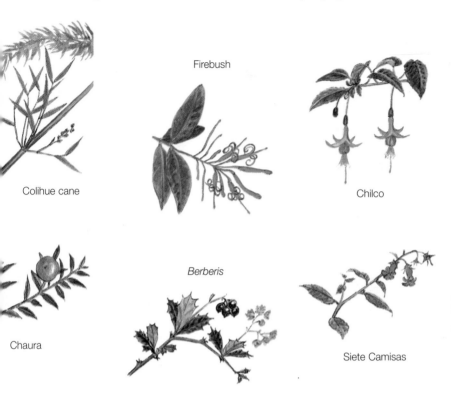

Colihue cane

Firebush

Chilco

Chaura

Berberis

Siete Camisas

Hemiparasites - page 62

Myzodendron

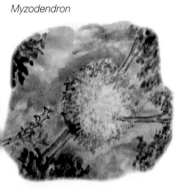

Quintral

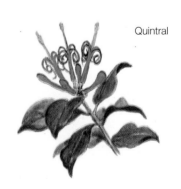

Lianas and creepers - page 63

Pil-pil Voqui

Botellita

Mutisia

Lichens - page 67

Old´s man beard

Fungus - page 68

Llao-llao

Amphibians - page 71

Darwin´s Frog

Reptiles - page 73

Liolaemus Li

ellan Woodpecker

Thorn-tailed
Rayadito

Chucao Tapaculo

een-backed
Firecrown

Austral
Parakeet

Austral
Thrush

Austral Pigmy Owl

Chilean Pigeon

Torrent Duck

V

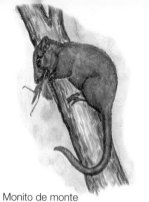

Monito de monte

Pudú

Bats
Murciélago
colorado

Huillín

Huemul

Red Fox

Beaver (exotic species)

Guiña cat